HOW TO CREATE A FAMILY BUSINESS IN MUSHROOM GROWING

Our family farm for growing delicious and medicinal mushrooms

GROWING EXOTIC MUSHROOMS FOR BEGINNERS AND PROFESSIONALS

Serge Honcharov & Nadiya Honcharova

TABLE OF CONTENTS

CHAPTER 1

To the Reader

Greetings, dear readers! If you have this book, you probably share our passion for mushrooms or are on the way to it. This book shares our love for mushrooms and experience in building a mushroom business. We invite you to the pages of our guide to explore the world of mushrooms.

This book will be helpful and engaging to readers who live in a private house with a small plot of land and a desire to start a home business. Nothing beats the pleasure of owning a profitable business right at home, without having to commute to work, being tied to a strict schedule, and working hours in the office. Creating your own business, especially when it is a common desire of the whole family, opens up many opportunities for you, and the creative process brings unique satisfaction and income.

Your time will be spent in the comfort of your home, where your whole family can reach their potential. If you value family comfort and are looking for a joint business idea, this book was created especially for you.

We present an exciting option for a family business: growing exotic mushrooms.

We created such a business at home and successfully developed it until it was interrupted by the war. The topic of growing mushrooms and using them as the basis for a family business attracts many. People turn to us for advice to get acquainted with the world of mushrooms and to learn how to organize a similar enterprise at home. Everyone loves that you can quickly and affordably organize everything in a small area and integrate it into your life.

The world of mushrooms enchants with its uniqueness, and many who met it once remain captivated forever, just like us. Therefore, we decided to share our experience with you, dear reader.

The book will interest both those who are just starting to get acquainted with mushroom growing and those who already have experience in it. After all, perfection is unlimited, and the expertise of colleagues is always enjoyable.

Besides, the book will be helpful to residents of ecovillages. Many turned to us for consultations to learn how to grow and consume mushrooms as an environmentally friendly and nutritious product alternative to animal protein. There is a wide range of mushrooms for cultivation, and knowledge of their characteristics will allow you to choose suitable crops, considering your region's labor costs and climatic factors. These will help you plan to save energy and get great results based on the knowledge from our book and experience.

Today, medicinal mushrooms are becoming increasingly popular due to numerous scientific facts about their beneficial effects on health. We also grew medicinal mushrooms, such as Lion's mane mushroom and Ganoderma. We were attracted to producing our mushrooms and using them to improve our quality of life. In addition, we have had many orders for these products. Therefore, fungotherapy lovers may also find our book helpful.

Our book will not refer to classical, long-known terms in mycology and biology, which have already been presented in numerous publications and are in the public domain. We aim to create a practical handbook for those interested in a mushroom farming business.

We have simplified the entire process of growing mushrooms for ourselves and will teach you how to master it just as quickly and affordably. The book will be filled with practical guidance based entirely on our personal experience, and the technological processes will be supplemented with detailed step-by-step photographs so that the reader can understand the process more realistically.

CHAPTER 2

About Us

We are Nadiya Honcharova and Serge Honcharov, a family from Ukraine who have devoted almost 20 years of our lives to commercial mushroom cultivation.

We worked as technologists at various mushroom productions, built and established new enterprises, created projects, and adjusted technologies.

We have many years of experience in this field and are ready to share interesting and valuable knowledge in our book. Mushroom growing was initially just a hobby for us. However, over time, it became more than just a hobby; it became a job and a field for creativity. Our family is a real team. Many experts in this field in Ukraine know us since mushroom growth in our country is on high level. We often act as speakers at various seminars, including such as UHPDB and UMDIS. In addition, I am a co-author of the works of Doctor of Science in Biology Iryna Bandura on the topic: *TECHNOLOGICAL PRINCIPLES FOR THE INTRODUCTION OF WINTER MUSHROOM (FLAMMULINA VELUTIPES (CURTIS) SINGER) INTO THE INDUSTRIAL CULTURE.*

We will bring to your attention a series of books that examine different levels of mushroom business: small (home or family, up to 2204 pounds of mushrooms per month), medium (up to 6613 pounds of mushrooms per month), and large (up to 22046-44092 pounds per month). All our books contain detailed copyright photographs, thanks to which many aspects of mushroom growing become clear and answer many questions.

We were lucky enough to build and put into operation all these levels of business in mushroom growing, so we are ready to share our experience in our publications.

The first book is dedicated to small, family businesses that can be created with minimal costs right at home.

My wife and I lack specialized training in mycology or biology, but we have vast practical experience in the mushroom-growing business.

Therefore, our practical knowledge will be more helpful. Expect the book's narrative to be practical rather than academic and, thus, more advantageous for you.

CHAPTER 3

Moving Home

Having lived and worked in various parts of Ukraine for over 15 years, we, mushroom growers, have always felt a strong desire to return home – to the Zaporizhzhia region in Ukraine. This place has long made us nostalgic, and we dreamed of creating our home mushroom production here. This dream accompanied us for several years when we were far from home.

In 2020, we decided to run a small business far from noisy and crowded production facilities. The new experience of a cozy family business attracted us. We moved from the big city to our house in a provincial town in the Zaporizhzhia region, located on the banks of the Kakhovka reservoir. Fresh and clean air filled us with strength for new beginnings. We were waiting for the construction of a mushroom complex, the arrangement of everyday life, and putting in order a plot with a large garden, a vineyard, and a vegetable garden. All this required our attention and care.

The initial capital was minimal, and we had to be very frugal, carefully planning every step. We based our plans on our experience and ability to do things quickly and with minimal investment. However, to fulfill our dream, we sacrificed our faithful friend – the motorcycle we covered thousands of kilometers on during our travels.

The priority was to construct a building for growing mushrooms and equip it with the necessary climate systems and equipment. Having extensive experience designing such objects, we understood that the vital point in such a project is the correct organization of the internal space. All work buildings and equipment should be designed to minimize movement during production, ensuring operational efficiency and labor savings.

We introduce you to our home production plan below.

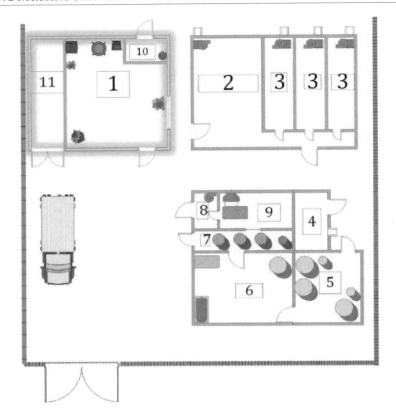

ESTATE PLAN WITH PRODUCTION PREMISES

1.Home

2.Incubator

3.Growing chambers

4.Refrigerator

5.Substrate preparation area

6.Raw materials warehouse

7.Sterilization room

8.Ventilation unit. Clean area locker room

9.Inoculation room

10.Boiler room

11.Garage

CHAPTER 4

Construction of a Cultivation Site

We decided to start building the complex with growing chambers, which became the first step toward our goal – creating a family business for growing mushrooms. Having launched the complex, we were able to start earning a living and accumulating funds for further development. It was the first phase of our project.

We built the complex in three months, which allowed us to start growing mushrooms the same year. We used a ready-made substrate for oyster mushrooms purchased from our colleagues in Melitopol. This choice of direction at the first stage justified itself.

Therefore, if anyone has the opportunity to start buying ready-made substrate blocks, we recommend this approach – first, build a growing complex, learn how to grow mushrooms on a purchased substrate, and then organize your substrate production.

The complex included a building consisting of three growth chambers, 20 m² (215 ft²) each, and one chamber for incubating substrate blocks, 60 m² (645 ft²). In total, the building occupied 120 m² (1291 ft²).

It was three yards from the house, the shortest route to work. I received great pleasure from being in a warm home, drinking aromatic tea, and instantly immersing myself in the atmosphere of autumn and the world of mushrooms in the cell.

I also loved waking up at night, grabbing a flashlight and a handheld climate controller, and going into the breeding chambers to observe our pets' lives. At this time, the fans of the air conditioning unit were making a steady noise. These sounds were like a mushroom symphony for me. I still often remember these sounds. Climate control systems created autumn in the cells, although it was winter, frost, and snow outside. The chamber air was filled with moisture, warmth, and the smell of mushrooms. Different cultures of mushrooms grew in each chamber, so they emitted different odors. And I, as a professional, always knew what our pets needed to make them feel comfortable and to make us happy with the harvest. Automation monitored climate parameters, but experience always suggested what needed to be corrected so that the harvest was maximum and of high quality.

Unfortunately, our farm lasted only two years. In the second year, when we were at the peak of production and successfully selling a variety of mushrooms, the war with the Russian Federation began. Early in the morning, when I was collecting Shiitake, we heard bomb explosions. That was happening 19km. (12 miles) from us. Then, the occupation began, and we had to leave our home and farm.

CHAPTER 5

Construction of a Growing Complex

We calculated the area for growing chambers based on the planned volume of mushroom production per month – 400-500 kg (881-1102lb). We needed 2-2,5 tons (4409-5511 pounds) of substrate to achieve this goal. We decided to build three chambers measuring 10x2m. (10x2 yards) to implement this task. These cells had shelves on both sides with one aisle in the middle. This arrangement of the premises allowed us to sequentially load the substrate under the fruiting cycle of the mushroom blocks and created ease of work inside the chambers. It ensured a stable supply of marketable mushrooms for sale throughout the month and maintained a clear production cycle throughout the season.

The incubator was designed in the same room as the growing chambers, which allowed us to load the chambers with the substrate without the extra effort of moving.

To reduce costs, we abandoned sandwich panels when constructing growing chambers and used expanded polystyrene sheets instead. The chambers were mounted on wooden beams and slats, after which the surface was plastered.

To create the structure of shelves for mushroom blocks, we decided to use wooden beams and boards since this material was the most accessible for us then.

The pictures show the construction sequence. After marking, we installed wooden posts made of beams measuring 50x50 mm inches and the corner posts 100x100 mm square inches.

The lower part of the racks was treated with an antiseptic and filled with concrete. The floor was filled with concrete after all the racks had been installed. The distance between the posts was chosen to easily install polystyrene foam panels measuring 2x1 m. (2x1 yards) and 4cm (4 inches) thick.

We made a gable roof from the same panels, which was then covered with material from an old billboard left over from some election campaign. This coating was relatively cheap and, in our experience, lasted up to 10 years. The outer wall of polystyrene foam panels was plastered with mesh adhesive, making it durable and waterproof.

Of course, if you have sufficient funds, you could use sandwich panels for the walls and roof.

These would simplify the construction process. However, given our financial limitations, we chose a more affordable option.

The result was a beautiful and economical building that fully met its objectives. It was easy to make and seal any technological holes in the panels for fans, windows, and doors, which made it possible to create a comfortable building and continue to improve it.

Each chamber also had an entrance door and a door at the end of the chamber for easy loading and unloading of spent blocks. The climate in the chamber was maintained by a homemade climate control unit (CU), to which I will devote a separate chapter. We faced the same task during its manufacture: to create a reliable, economical installation from available materials and elements.

Installing windows and doors

Installation of external walls made of polystyrene foam

Completion of construction

Covering the roof with billboard material

CHAPTER 6

Design of the Air Conditioning Unit (CU)

The climate control system must include air heating, ventilation, humidification, and cooling. In addition, it is necessary to ensure the ability to regulate the ratio of fresh and recirculated air. Monitoring and managing these climate parameters in the mushroom growing chamber will give the mushrooms full functioning to obtain a high-quality harvest in the planned volumes. It is important to note that each type of mushroom requires specific climate parameters, so the climate control system must be capable of creating a variety of conditions.

Moreover, when growing different types of mushrooms in one chamber, it is essential to provide each species with conditions for comfortable growth. Working with the climate control system requires some skill and careful attention, but in the end, it will be an exciting and enjoyable experience when you see the result of your work.

The task of the climate control system is to create and regulate the necessary climate parameters for mushroom life, such as maintaining optimal temperature, humidity, and carbon dioxide levels and regulating air flows. It is also crucial to ensure that appropriate relations between all these parameters can be maintained. On large farms, industrial and expensive climate systems are usually used for these purposes. However, we set ourselves to develop and create a similar installation at minimal cost.

The central heating element was an inexpensive radiator from any old car. I used a Moskvich car (USSR). It was good because it was cheap, but most importantly, it was made of copper, with durable copper honeycombs and a sufficiently large gap between the lamellas of these honeycombs. All the 1970s and 1980s old cars had similar radiators, and they can easily be found on the secondary market.

They could also be easily soldered for repair or reconstruction.

At first glance, the photo shows a primitive but efficient structure, which had already completed the season and was dismantled for inspection.

A standard axial fan with a 300-350mm. (11-13 inches) diameter, made in China, works reliably in humid camera conditions and is IP-65 protected. It is attached to the car radiator through a diffuser. Similar fans are available in a wide range.

Single-phase 220V fans are connected to the network through a simple power regulator, which allows you to adjust the fan speed, thus changing its performance. It is perfect because we need different airflow for mushroom cultures and stages of their development.

A thermal water main was installed through all the chambers from a domestic gas boiler, which heated the house and was sufficient to heat the growing chambers and incubator. The radiators were connected to this line through a two-way valve with a servo drive, which a simple temperature controller controlled. Later, the system was converted to a three-way valve, but we only have photos of the first version.

An inexpensive Chinese faucet with a 220V servo drive and a simple electronic thermostat on ds18b20 sensors made it possible to maintain the chamber`s temperature quite accurately, within -1/0,5C° (30/33°F) degree. Everything worked very reliably all season. At the end of the season, all elements were cleared of spores and mucus, preserved, and ready to work again next season.

The radiator's output power can reach 70 kW at a circulating water temperature of about +100°C (212°F). However, we could not provide such a high coolant temperature because of the limitations of the gas boiler, which can only supply water up to +85°C (185°F).

Nevertheless, at a temperature of +80°C (176°F), the radiator heat exchanger quickly produced thermal power of up to 20-30 kW.

It is important to note that the thermal performance of our climate control system is more than sufficient for a chamber with a volume of 60m² (78 cubic yards). For example, when I tested this setup in a 100m² (1076-square)-feet room without partitions, I could maintain a temperature of +20°C (68°F) while it was -5°C (23°F) outside. However, no mushroom blocks were in the room, which usually added heat to the chamber due to internal heating.

These ballpark figures are helpful for those planning to determine the size of their nursery facilities. The ability to smoothly control the fan's speed and tap with a servo drive allowed the air conditioning unit to successfully maintain the required temperature and level of airflow. If you need to increase the overall power of the installation, then it is enough to install two or even three radiators in series, one after another. Thus, you will increase the overall power but not the maximum dimensions of the installation.

Protecting the radiator from fungal spores plays a central role in ensuring the efficiency of the climate system. It is crucial to provide this protection when growing mushrooms such as Oyster mushroom, which produces more spores than others.

For this purpose, an effective serviceable filter was developed that was easy to clean and wash without interrupting the work process. The filter, through which air flowed, was installed in front of the radiator and was a double frame that opened like a book. A mosquito net was installed on the frame, which created the first barrier for fungal spores. Two layers of heifer shade netting were placed between the frames, also known as a mesh bag for packing vegetables. This filter design ensured the retention of spores and protected the radiator honeycombs from contamination.

Filter cleaning and washing were carried out every 1-2 days during active mushroom fruiting when more spores were released. This procedure took only a few minutes, and thanks to the radiator protection against fungal spores, I have always had confidence in the entire system's performance.

This structural element is visible in the photo.

Installation of air conditioning system

Serviceable filter design to protect the radiator from spores

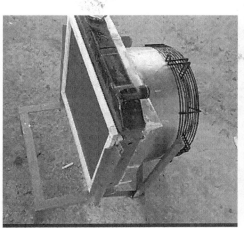

Air conditioning units that have worked for one season and are prepared for revision for the next season

CHAPTER 7

Air Humidification System

We examined only one of the main components of the climate control system, which includes an air heating unit and a ventilation unit. As you can see, everything here is effortless and inexpensive.

Next, after heating, the air must be humidified to the required humidity parameters. We will talk about the humidity parameters themselves, their effect on the growth of mushrooms, and the intricacies of managing and monitoring them in the following chapters. Now, let's look at the technical solution to this problem.

Indeed, air humidification is essential in creating optimal conditions for fungal growth.

Several basic humidification systems can be used in grow rooms:

1. **Hydropneumatic nozzles:** These nozzles work on the principle of water pressure and compressed air to spray water into tiny droplets in the air. It is an effective way to humidify the air in the chambers.

2. **High-pressure injectors:** These nozzles spray water into fine droplets but operate at a higher pressure to ensure a more even water distribution.

3. **Ultrasonic humidification** cassettes use ultrasound to atomize water into tiny particles. They provide high humidification efficiency and reasonable distribution of moisture in the air.

4. **Centrifugal humidifier:** This system rotates unique elements to spray water into the air. It provides uniform hydration and good performance.

5. **Low-pressure injectors (LP injectors):** These nozzles create fog in vegetable greenhouses and humidify the air in mushroom growing chambers.

The choice of a specific humidification system depends on many factors, including chamber size, humidity requirements, budget, and technical capabilities. Each system has advantages and disadvantages, and choosing the best option requires careful analysis and discussion.

  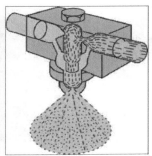

Air humidification with hydropneumatic nozzles is a well-known humidification method in growing rooms.

Air humidification with hydropneumatic nozzles is a well-known humidification method in growing rooms.

Advantages:

1. **Rapid dissolution of water particles in the air:** The high rate of water particle release from the nozzle allows them to dissolve quickly, providing adequate humidification. The size of the water particle is approximately 20-50 microns.

2. **Ease of maintenance:** The nozzles are usually easy to maintain and can adjust the water-air torch, which ensures ease of operation.

Flaws:

1. **Availability of an air compressor:** An air compressor is required to operate hydropneumatic nozzles, which is an additional costly element and requires systematic maintenance. The pressure in the airline is 0,3-0,5 MPa (43-72 psi), and the pressure in the water line is 0,1-0,3 MPa (14-43 psi).

2. **Noise and the need to remove the compressor:** Due to the noise emitted by the compressor, its installation must be moved outside the chambers to a separate room, which can complicate the installation and connection process.

3. **Main complexity:** The main going to the nozzles should consist of two lines – air and water. It complicates the installation process and requires additional costs for materials and maintenance.

High-pressure injectors

Air humidification with high-pressure nozzles is an effective method characterized by the following features:

Advantages:

1.**Efficiency:** The system is highly efficient due to the water droplet size ranging from 5 to 10 microns, which ensures good air humidification.

2. **Easy to install:** The quick-release connections make the system easy to install and are widely used in large enterprises, including champignon-growing enterprises. The system can lay long lines and use only one high-pressure channel. Mounting and installation are also simplified.

3. **Low maintenance requirements:** The nozzles require little maintenance, mainly thanks to the ceramic nozzle parts requiring little to no cleaning.

4. **Flexibility in choosing a water source:** In some cases, you can do without special water treatment, although this depends on the water quality.

Flaws:

1. **Expensive system:** The high cost of the high-pressure pump makes the entire system expensive. Due to its noise, pump requires regular maintenance and installation in a separate room.

Air humidification with high-pressure nozzles is generally adequate but requires significant investment in pumps and maintenance.

Ultrasonic humidification cassettes

Ultrasonic humidification (UH) cassettes are an effective humidification system for growing chambers with many features:

Advantages:

1.**Small droplet size:** This system produces the smallest water droplets, ranging from 1 to 5 microns, which ensures good air humidification.

2. **Easy to install and operate:** This system operates quietly and does not require complex water transmission lines. Laying the line to the container tank where the cassette is located and connecting through the shut-off valve is sufficient for its operation.

3. **It does not require mains:** Unlike other humidification methods, ultrasonic cassettes do not require water transmission lines, making their installation more straightforward and economical.

4. **Efficiency:** A cassette of 10 membranes can produce 5 liter (1.3 gallon) of cold steam per hour, enough to humidify a chamber with a volume of 100-120m² (130-156 cubic yards).

Flaws:

1. **Water requirements:** Water for this system must be pre-prepared, and its quality must be brought to 100ppm.

2. **Low steam speed:** At a growing temperature of +14-18°C (57-64°F), the speed of movement of the cold fog through the chamber is shallow, which can lead to the deposition of droplets on the surface of the mushrooms in the form of condensation and disruption of the mushrooms' respiration.

3. **The need to ensure the dissolution of droplets in the air:** It is recommended to install the cassette as high as possible in the air preparation air channel so that the droplets have time to dissolve in

the air to prevent from depositing on the surface of the mushrooms in the form of condensation.

4. **Cost:** The average price of a cassette is $100, and a 220/48V power supply is $30.

Overall, ultrasonic humidification cassettes are an effective and convenient humidification system for grow rooms, although they require some adjustment and maintenance.

Centrifugal humidifier

A centrifugal humidifier (CHH) is not a very convenient humidification system. Droplet size is 10-20 microns. However, installing such a system in an air duct is complicated.

Therefore, it is installed directly in the chamber, which can lead to condensation of water droplets on the surface of the mushrooms. The distribution of droplets throughout the entire chamber volume is also heterogeneous. The durability of such an installation directly depends on the quality and durability of the engine itself, which must operate in a damp environment.

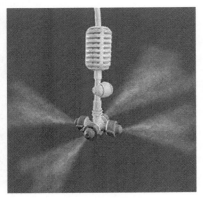

Low-pressure nozzles (LPN) have a droplet size of 100-200 microns. Using such nozzles directly in the growing chamber is difficult since large drops do not have time to dissolve in the air and settle as condensation on the mushrooms, which is unacceptable. However, their use in mushroom growing is still acceptable, and I have successfully used them for some time.

The nozzles must be placed directly in the air channel made of a polyethylene sleeve. In this case, the droplet volume is mixed with a strong vortex airflow for some time, and sufficient droplets have time to dissolve. Undissolved drops are drained into a return container as return water.

You can also place the nozzle at the maximum height between the rows and direct the torches along them. If set up correctly, a satisfactory and inexpensive humidification system can be achieved, although this may be a temporary solution.

The cost of such nozzles is approximately 3-4 dollars, which should be added to the price of a coarse and fine filter.

Washing machine valves are used to control low-pressure nozzles.

In future books, we will examine humidification and cooling systems using adiabatic cooling panels (ACPs). We decided to split a separate chapter on this topic because ACPs are a very effective and affordable solution widely used in industrial mushroom growing. We have successfully used these panels in our enterprises.

Considering the cost-effectiveness, ease of installation, and significant energy savings of adiabatic cooling panels, we decided to pay special attention to them. This will allow our readers to understand the benefits of this technology over other, more expensive methods of humidification and cooling. Our goal is to create an efficient and cost-effective production. Therefore, we will carefully consider all aspects of the equipment that will help us save money during the construction of the complex and its subsequent operation.

We have extensive practical experience using such panels and will happily share this experience with our readers.

CHAPTER 8

Design and Installation of a Humidification System.

We considered various options for humidification systems. Now, I will focus more on the system we chose for our air conditioning unit: an ultrasonic humidification cassette.

The operating principle of this installation has long been known.

Ceramic membranes in the cassette emit ultrasound, which breaks water into tiny particles ranging from 1 to 5 microns. These particles create a thick fog, which, when further dissolved in the air, allows the mushrooms to achieve the necessary humidity.

The photo shows a humidification unit with a cassette and a 48-volt power supply. Such units are manufactured in China and readily available on different online platforms. The average cost of a cassette with 10 membranes, enough to provide humidity in one chamber, is about $100, and a power supply is about $30.

Now, let's look at the complete design of the humidification unit in our air conditioning unit.

This unit was as simple and inexpensive as the heating part of the air conditioner. In general, this unit is a plastic barrel with a volume of 53 gallons, in the bottom of which an ultrasonic humidification cassette (US) is installed. Any water shut-off valve is installed in the barrel to maintain the required water level above the surface of the cassette. In our case, it is from the flush tank to which the main water is supplied. The humidifier barrel is connected to the heating and ventilation unit through a diffuser, which is manufactured and cut to a template from stainless or galvanized sheet steel. The diameter of this diffuser should be approximately equal to the diameter of the fan's impeller used. The barrel diffuser is connected to the fan using a strip of soft material to eliminate vibrations and friction.

In this case, a simple strip of polyethylene was used. A viewing window made of transparent plastic was made at the front of the barrel to observe and control the fog formation process.

Manufacturing a diffuser for connection to an air conditioning system. Installation of viewing window

Connecting the humidification unit to the air conditioning unit

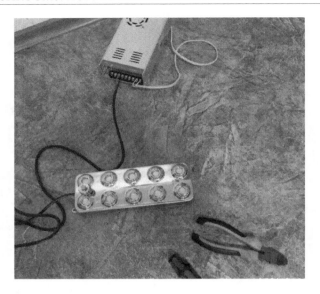

Ultrasonic humidification cassette with power supply

Air conditioning system in operation

So, what happens when we connect the heating and ventilation unit of the heat exchanger with the humidification unit (barrel)?

A fan directs the heated air into the barrel, where an ultrasonic cassette forms a powerful water mist. This mist is mixed with the heated air in the barrel, and this air-water mixture can be directed further into the growing chamber.

To distribute the prepared heated and humidified air, a 39-inches-wide polyethylene sleeve is used, which is placed on the neck of the barrel and positioned vertically. The upper end of the sleeve is tied and suspended from the chamber's ceiling. Air nozzles made from plastic drink cups are installed on the vertical part of the sleeve to discharge the air-water mixture into the chamber. Their number depends on the diameter of the bottom of the cups and can range from 5 to 10 pieces. Nozzles move directional air through the chamber along the rows with mushroom substrate blocks.

The diameter of the sleeve should be chosen at least a specific size, and it is better to make it as large as possible to create a sufficiently large volume of the polyethylene cylinder. In this volume, vortex air flows occur, in which water particles from the fog dissolve well, which is extremely important for the final quality of the prepared air.

I will dwell on one crucial point. The operation of the ultrasonic cassette necessarily requires water treatment. The water must be freed from hard impurities, which otherwise will be deposited on the membranes. It is achieved quickly if the water is fed through a filter with ion exchange resin. Such cassette filters are available for sale and installed in a standard flask for water filtering (see photo).

This set was enough work for three months. Then, the cartridge could easily be regenerated using ordinary table salt and was ready for use.

However, there are cases when the water in the system is already so clean that it does not require additional water treatment, and everything works fine all season. This optimal balance between water quality and water treatment requirements can be determined during operation by monitoring the operation of the installation and the quality of the air received.

CHAPTER 9

Cooling System Design

The cooling unit in the climate control system plays a key role, especially in mushroom-growing conditions. In our version, we use window-built-in air conditioners since conventional split systems are not suitable because the heat exchanger fins are very close to each other. It does not allow divided systems in damp rooms with many spores. However, window air conditioners have significant gaps between the radiator fins, which makes them an ideal choice for our situation.

In our version, I used old Soviet BK-2500 air conditioners. They are available at low prices on the secondary market and are highly reliable. Similar air conditioners can be easily found on the secondary market in the USA and Europe.

The window air conditioner is installed close to the heating radiator of the air conditioning system. Cold flows from the air conditioner are captured by the fan, mixed with the chamber air, and fed further through the humidification system through the hose into the chamber. Also, in the summer, an auto-radiator can supply cold water from a well with a temperature of +10-15°C (50-59°F). This combination will significantly reduce energy consumption for cooling the air in the chamber during the hot season.

Installation of an external air conditioner in the cooling system of the growing chamber.

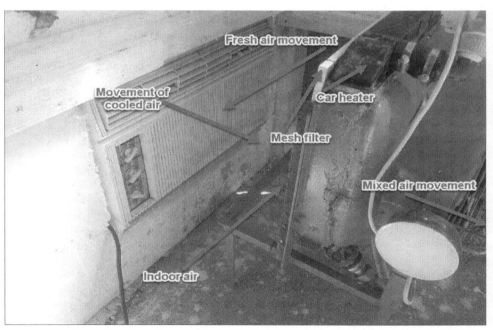

Docking of cooling, heating, and ventilation elements of the growing chamber.

Installing an air conditioner in the cooling system

Cable entry. View of the air conditioner from outside the chamber

As a result, we have all the necessary components for an air conditioning system: heating, cooling, humidification, and airflow.

Gravity blinds are installed in the same plane as the air conditioner to allow fresh air to enter the chamber. Air enters the chamber through them when some vacuum is created inside. It will enable you to effectively exchange air in the chamber and maintain optimal conditions for mushroom growth.

Thus, the carbon dioxide level is controlled using a CO2 controller. When the CO2 level exceeds the set value, the exhaust fan turns on, creating a slight vacuum in the chamber and opening the gravity shutters to allow fresh air to enter. It will enable you to maintain optimal conditions for mushroom growth. The power of the exhaust fan is 20-40 W, which is significantly less than the power of the main fan.

Connecting the exhaust fan through a power regulator lets you control its operation effectively, depending on current needs.

For now, I have described the conceptual design of the CU, which is very simple and made from inexpensive components. As a result, I created four such installations, which fully provided the necessary climate for our three fruiting chambers and incubator.

These climate control systems provided us with stable parameters, temperature, humidity, and CO2 levels, which made it possible to grow excellent commercial mushrooms for sale.

One of the chambers had an additional longitudinal ventilation sleeve. Oyster mushrooms were grown in this chamber, which required more intense air movement along the substrate blocks.

I'll also add that I have sufficient experience in electrical engineering and electronics, so connecting all the elements to simple controllers was not difficult.

The photo shows some of my designs on simple controllers, of which a massive variety is on sale. I do not claim an industrial level of manufacturing. The main thing is that it all worked reliably and was very inexpensive.

 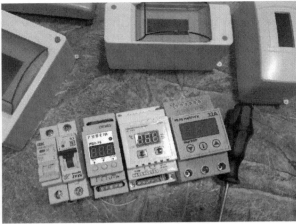

Humidity and temperature controller. Assembling automation using simple controllers

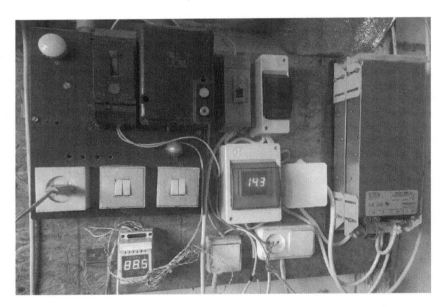

Climate control panel

As a result, I spent about $400 on manufacturing one climate control system. Despite its simplicity and seeming primitiveness, it was very reliable and effective.

This entire complex is shown in the picture.

CHAPTER 10

Growing Oyster Mushrooms on Purchased Substrate

We quickly moved towards our primary goal – creating a family mushroom-growing business. Having built a growing chamber and equipped it with climate systems, we were ready to grow mushrooms on substrates purchased from our colleagues. At this stage, we started with the cultivation of oyster mushrooms. We have sufficient experience in this area thanks to the well-developed mushroom market in Ukraine, with which we are very familiar.

We started by growing mushrooms on a substrate we purchased from our colleagues. These substrate blocks are manufactured using non-sterile technology and weigh about 15kg. (33lb) each. This substrate production method is typical for many large enterprises, which produce it end masse in thousands of pounds per day. We already had experience growing oyster mushrooms using a similar technology, so nothing was unexpected.

Using original technology for loading such blocks in our chambers, we achieved a substrate loading density of up to 5tons (11023 pounds) in each chamber with an area of 20m² (215 square) feet. It is a very high density, allowing us to obtain large harvest volumes. Besides, blocks stacked one on top of the other could heat themselves and the fruiting chamber, significantly saving heating resources.

Oyster mushroom substrate blocks from our partners. That is the number of blocks that weigh 5 tons and fit into one chamber.

Laying substrate blocks

Oyster mushroom fruiting

Harvest for Christmas

That is such beauty

Record breakers

Ready for shipment

CHAPTER 11

Reconstruction of Growing Chambers

So, our first winter season of 2021 has passed. Like most businesses in Ukraine, the commercial mushroom season ends in early May. The demand for mushrooms is decreasing as seasonal vegetables and fruits appear on the market, and enterprises reduce work intensity or go on holidays.

For us, this is the time to continue reconstruction and our path to the main goal – launching an entire production cycle from mycelium and substrate to various types of mushrooms packaged for sale.

All chambers were cleared of production activities from the previous season, materials were purchased, and a work plan and project were drawn up. We again plunged into the creative process of creation. First, we reconstructed the growing chambers. Then, the ceilings were insulated with another layer of polystyrene foam boards, and new racks and shelves were installed. Now, everything has been designed with sterile substrate preparation technology in mind. The design of the shelves was presented in step-by-step photographs.

The reconstruction of the second stage of construction begins. Installation of new shelves in growing chambers

Additional insulation of the ceiling saves significant energy costs

The shelves are ready, the air conditioning unit is running, the blocks are on the shelves, and we are starting a new season

The longitudinal additional air duct in one of the chambers

CHAPTER 12

Substrate Production Area

The substrate production site was the next step in our plan. Given our experience and knowledge of this field, we chose sterile technology as the most reliable and practical. Our entire compact home system has been designed with this technology in mind.

We will examine this technology in detail in the following chapters, but for now, I will only say that it allows you to create substrates for all Xylotrophs. These wood-decaying fungi comprise the main range of commercial fungal cultures on the market. Using sterile technology, we can vary the choice of raw materials, including agricultural waste, which expands possibilities and reduces production costs.

We studied the market for available raw materials in our region and chose what best suited our needs. We will examine this aspect of substrates in more detail in the chapter.

The substrate production area includes three zones: a zone for mixing and packaging the substrate composition, where a small part of the raw materials was also stored for ease of work. The second zone is a conditionally clean zone where the sterilizers were located. The third zone is a clean room for introducing mycelium into sterile blocks.

We have created special sterilizers to sterilize the substrate, the design of which is given in more detail below.

CHAPTER 13

Overview of Sterilizer Design

In my practice, I previously made sterilizers for an enterprise that could produce several blocks for experiments and testing technologies. It was my invention, which proved to be very positive.

The original version was modernized during its work.

As a result, I brought this design to perfection while maintaining a minimum cost for its production.

I'll tell you all the details of its manufacturing technology and the subtleties of operation.

Again, the main thing is to adhere to the principle of producing an inexpensive yet reliable design.

The sterilizer's essence is the atmospheric sterilization of substrate blocks at a temperature of +100°C (212°F) in a "flowing steam" environment. In other words, it treats substrate blocks with steam at a constant temperature of +100°C (212°F) for 6-10 hours. It's a steam generator.

This method has many advantages. First, there is no need to use an expensive autoclave or work with high-pressure vessels, often associated with specific difficulties. Second, when atmospheric sterilizing substrates, you can use cheaper polyethylene bags that can withstand temperatures of +100°C (212°F) well. In contrast, when using an autoclave, the heat treatment temperature can reach +120°C (248°F). This mode requires polypropylene bags, which are much more expensive and significantly increase the cost of the substrate.

The sterilizer was designed to use 200-liter (53-gallon) barrels, initially intended for glycerin. These barrels have been thoroughly washed and prepared for use. The inner surface of the barrels was coated with varnish, which lasted for at least three seasons. The cost of one such barrel was about 10 dollars.

So, three sterilizer barrels were manufactured, which ensured a continuous process of loading and sterilizing substrate blocks. It allowed us to produce a substrate batch daily without downtime or delays.

The photo report clearly shows the metalworking process of making a sterilizer, so I will not describe this process in detail. Instead, I will discuss the practical details of setting up and operating the sterilizer.

Typically, such sterilizers use stainless steel floats to automatically maintain the water level required for the electric heater's operation. I also made such floats but faced high material and manufacturing costs. In addition, it turned out that you could do without them, which made the sterilizer's design more accessible and simplified the work with it.

However, certain conditions must be met to bypass the use of floats. One is related to the design of the sterilizer itself, and the other to its operation.

CHAPTER 14

Design Details and Operation Algorithm of the Sterilizer

The height of the water level to the lower false bottom should be 4 inches. The power of the heating element should be 1.5-2.0 kW. A fitting with a tap for steam release is mounted in the sterilizer lid. Steam is discharged through a metal-plastic tube, at least 3m (11 inches) long, located at an angle to the barrel at approximately 45°C degrees. The steam will escape through this tube and condense, and the condensate will flow back into the barrel. Thus, water loss from the container will be minimal. It means there will be enough water for the entire heat treatment cycle, which is about 10 hours, and there will be no need to add it constantly. In addition, there is no need to supply main water to the barrel since it will be enough to add water once before sterilization.

Many of my colleagues repeated the sterilizer's design, and all had consistently good results.

The sterilizer worked perfectly without adding water and had excellent temperature performance. In such sterilizers, we consistently obtained excellent-quality substrate blocks.

Now, here are some essential tips regarding the electrical part. After loading the blocks into the barrel, the heating element is turned on at full power. Then we wait for stable steam to exit from the outlet. When using a heating element with a power of 1.5 kW, this occurs after about 4 hours, and with 2.0 kW – after about 3 hours.

After a stable steam output, it is necessary to reduce the power of the heating element to 0.75-1.0 kW. It can be done by connecting a powerful 10-20A diode in series into the circuit. After this, the power of the heating element will decrease by approximately half.

More precise regulation can be achieved using a dimmer or power regulator widely available on the Chinese market. These devices are inexpensive and easy to connect. Voltage adjustment allows you to gain more accurate vaporization parameters.

Later, I equipped the sterilizers with timers, making automating the process possible. I called it "set it and forget it." After the sterilizer was ready, I started the timer, and it took over the entire process.

Since we finished work closer to 21:00, I could calmly go to bed, knowing that the timer would control all processes. Such timers are sold widely, and anyone who understands electrical engineering can organize a similar system for themselves.

If all the specified conditions are met, the initial water level, 10cm. (4 inches) high, will be sufficient for the entire heat treatment cycle.

However, if desired, you can equip your sterilizer with a water float. I was delighted with my design, so I didn't need to change anything.

The photo shows all these options. Take the concept itself as a basis and implement your ideas. As a result, we received three sterilizers, in each of which we could place 60-64 blocks of 1,4-1,6 kg (3-3.5) pounds each for sterilization. Thus, we received about 100kg (220 pounds) of substrate every day.

That may not seem like much to some, but it is enough to eventually produce up to 500kg (1102 pounds) of marketable mushrooms. Let's count together. For 25 days a month, we produced 2500kg (5511 pounds) of substrate. With an actual yield of 20%, we got the planned 500kg (1102 pounds) of mushrooms. This indicator was our calculated productivity.

And the most important thing! My wife and I worked together and did not hire an additional worker. It was the primary condition we set for ourselves. But suppose you have a family in which, in addition to you, some children are interested in success, and everyone is working towards an expected result. In that case, all indicators can be doubled, tripled, or even more. It all depends on desire and aspiration. After all, that's what a family business is for.

Only our granddaughter Lilya could help us. This could happen only during the summer holidays, when we have more time to work together, laugh, and listen to music.

Now, we have dealt with an essential stage in the technological process, such as the arrangement of the sterilization site. The photographs clearly show how it all looked in working mode. Later, we installed a 50 Liter (13-gallon) autoclave in this room.

It was high-quality equipment that was still produced in the USSR. It was also inexpensive, only about $100.

It was intended for mycelium production, but we will discuss this later in the following chapters.

The barrels for the sterilizer have arrived

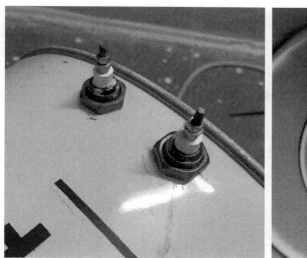
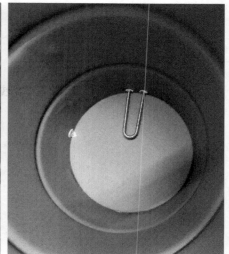

Installing the heater

Installation of the drain fitting

Protective cover

Heater with casing and power regulator

Power regulator

Insulating sterilizers with foam

CHAPTER 15

Construction of a Clean Zone

The next area of our farm is the clean room, also known as the inoculation area.

Blocks that have already undergone sterilization enter here through a transfer gateway to introduce planting mycelium of a mushroom culture into each of them. This process, known as inoculation, is essential and exciting. It is at this moment that mushroom life begins in each block. You can already imagine how the long-awaited mushrooms will appear from these blocks in one or two months.

This project is one of the most expensive in terms of the budget during construction. However, it is crucial to design all elements of this zone correctly.

The stability of the entire production process and ease of operation depend on this.

As the name suggests, an air filtration system keeps a clean room (or zone) as clean as possible. It is necessary to prevent pathogenic microorganisms from entering the substrate block during mycelium inoculation. To avoid contaminating the entire substrate batch, refrain from compromising standard technological measures.

Among the main pathogen competitors are Trichoderma, olive mold, mucor, Neurospora, and others. If they enter a sterile block, they can outpace the growth of fungal mycelium and entirely or partially capture the substrate, which means such blocks must be disposed of.

Therefore, planning and constructing a clean area carefully and strictly adhering to operating procedures is essential. That includes sanitizing, using clean clothing, gloves, masks, tools, and more. Next, we will examine all aspects of the production process in detail.

For now, let's return to the construction of the second stage of the home farm, namely, the start of construction of the clean zone.

The photographs trace the entire stage of construction from the very beginning. I specifically posted pictures of the premises in their initial terrible form so that the reader could see that even from premises unsuitable for this, something significant can be made if there is a desire. The main thing is to have this motivation.

These premises previously housed laying hens, quails, and a workshop. Now, we had to turn them into a clean zone. We carried out a redevelopment that suited our objectives. We dismantled and moved windows and doors, installed partitions, and installed a transfer window gateway.

The old building has acquired a new look and life.

We already had the experience that allowed us to present the finished object, and we confidently moved towards its completion, step by step.

Of course, we had to replace the floors with a two-component varnish, although it would have been enough to lay ceramic tiles. I just had this varnish in stock.

The walls were plastered, the ceiling was lined with gypsum boards, and everything was covered with acrylic paint with silicone; this paint is resistant to disinfectants and ultraviolet treatment. At this point, the construction part was completed.

Start of construction of a clean room for block inoculation

Technological partition and transfer gateway

Completion of the construction part of the reconstruction

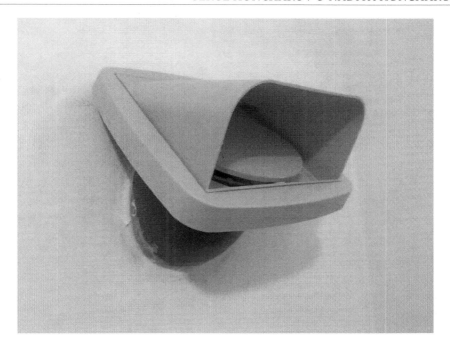

Relief valve

Almost everything done

CHAPTER 16

Manufacturing of HEPA Filter Box

Next, you must equip the room with ventilation using HEPA filters for fine air purification.

It is also crucial to prevent the presence of stagnant zones so that mold, the worst enemy of the substrate, cannot settle there in the future. Since the room always has high humidity, mold can quickly form in stagnant areas. The ventilation was designed so air could move in all corners, dead-end areas, and relief valves were installed in the walls to prevent mold.

We also need to install an inoculation table with a HEPA box. Here, the mycelium will be sown into substrate blocks in a stream of clean filtered air. These HEPA boxes can be purchased ready-made on the Chinese market and are usually very high quality. We often worked in factories where exactly such units were installed.

However, we were limited in funds for its acquisition, time, and the size of our inoculation zone.

So, I had to do everything myself. I ordered a galvanized iron dome from a tinsmith, purchased the HEPA filter itself, and the filter box was ready within a couple of days. All left was to attach PVC curtains and hang them over the inoculation table. The photo shows the entire sequence of actions.

An essential detail in the box`s design is an air divider. It is made of mesh and prevents directed airflow from directly hitting the HEPA filter. This directional flow could damage an expensive filter, so this node needs to be given special attention. Everything is visible in the photographs.

It is just the first stage. Now, I had to design the ventilation system itself.

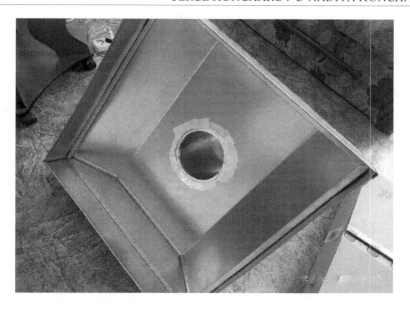

The HEPA filter dome has arrived

Installing a mesh to cut the airflow

Receiving a HEPA filter order

We have a helper, the cat Cupcake

Installing a filter in the air box

Sealing everything with silicone sealant

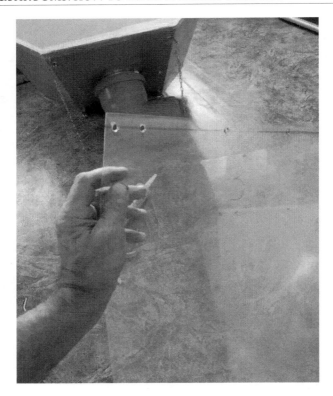

Guide curtains for laminar airflow

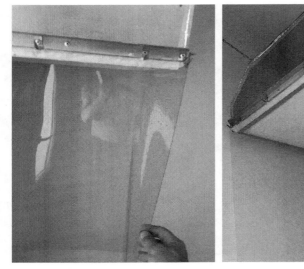

Making the curtains removable

CHAPTER 17

Clean Room Ventilation and Filtration System

Manufacturing a ventilation and air purification system for an inoculation room involves several key steps.

1. **HEPA box:** The first stage was the production of a HEPA box. This box performs two main functions: purifying outdoor air for the entire room and creating a laminar-filtered airflow in the area for sowing substrate blocks. Thus, we were able to combine two crucial elements in one device, which significantly reduced the cost of the ventilation system.

2. **Pre-filters:** Typically, G4 and F7 level pre-filters are installed in front of the HEPA filter, which increases its service life. However, factory prefilters are large, which is unsuitable for our small inoculation room.

3. **Design of pre-filters:** Our inoculation room requires pre-filters, but standard sizes are unsuitable. So, we decided to design them ourselves to fit the size of our room. It allowed us to optimize the use of space and reduce costs.

4. **Installation and testing:** After the prefilters are manufactured, they will be installed in front of the HEPA filter in the HEPA box. Once installed, the ventilation system will be tested to ensure efficiency and meet clean air requirements in the inoculation room. Only after successful testing will the system be ready for use.

5. **Regular maintenance:** The ventilation system requires regular maintenance and filter replacement to maintain a high level of air cleanliness in the room. This includes cleaning and replacing the pre-filters and HEPA filters per the manufacturer's recommendations.

Thus, creating a ventilation and air purification system for the inoculation room is an important step that provides the necessary conditions for a successful inoculation process and protects against infection by pathogenic microorganisms.

And, as always, we had to invent everything and make it from what we had at hand.

I picked up a suitable-sized box with latches from an old army radio station in the garage and began placing pre-filters. Strictly speaking, the G4 filter is an ordinary padding polyester fabric. Agrofibre fabric (spun bond) worked well as an F7 filter. I cut out frames from the mesh onto which I attached these materials. As a result, such filter cassettes could quickly be taken out of the box and serviced.

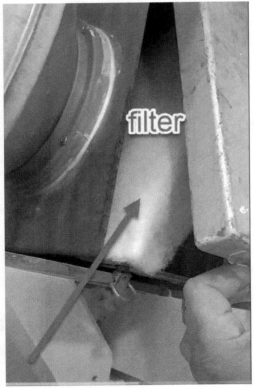

Everything worked out great, and I was pleased with the result.

Work progressed.

Next, I calculated and purchased the required parameters for a duct fan.

All these elements (HEPA box, pre-filter, fan) must be assembled into a single system of ventilation pipes and ducts. Sewer pipes with a diameter of 200 mm (8 inches) were suitable as pipes. Air relief valves were also installed in the expected stagnant zones.

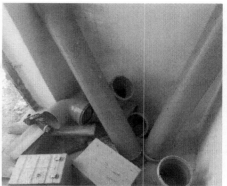

Clean room ventilation unit assembly

HEPA box and inoculation table

Plan a diagram of a clean area with a ventilation and air filtration system.

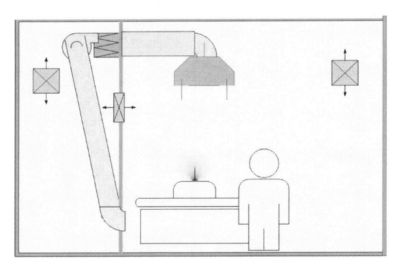

The cleanroom ventilation system includes filtration of fresh and recirculated air. This ratio is regulated by a damper and selected to create excess pressure in the room. It will not allow outside unpurified air to enter the room. We also flow clean filtered air from a HEPA box above the table where we sow the blocks.

We were able to achieve all these conditions with one installation. That is, we filter the internal air and mix a certain amount of external air into it, which allows us to create excess pressure in the room.

Everything turned out simple and inexpensive.

Finally, the first launch was made.

Everything worked perfectly, and we were pleased with the result. All I had to do was install a power regulator on the fan to regulate its speed and connect a bactericidal lamp.

Also, for convenience, the lamp was connected via a timer. It must automatically start an hour before entering a clean area.

It was not complicated for me; finally, everything was ready for a full launch.

My wife Nadya was especially pleased with the work results because inoculation is her responsibility, and she had to work there. Therefore, if everything is done correctly, it will be as convenient for her to work.

We were already looking forward to producing the first batch of substrate blocks.

Everything is ready to inoculate the blocks.

CHAPTER 18

Substrate Block Production Site

The substratum area, from which the entire production process begins, completed our reconstruction of the premises. We immediately considered all the aspects of the upcoming work in the planning to make everything as simple and easy as possible.

In general, this is where the entire production process begins its cycle. Here is where the future of the substrate block is laid.

The plan was to purchase a small substrate mixer. But several problems appeared at once.

The first thing is that even for a small (0.5 Cubicmeter) mixer, an engine with a power of about 5-6 kW was needed. Our home network could not handle such power. Moreover, other consumers, such as sterilizers, ventilation, etc., also participate in production.

There was an option to order a mixer for a gasoline engine. But this is an individual order, and the wait is long. On top of that, it's all quite expensive. And I remind you that our goal is to create a farm with minimal costs. There is an excellent version of a hand mixer called the "Drunk Barrel." I will present a photo of such a design here. If you search the Internet, you will understand what it is and its principle of operation.

Mixer Drunk Barrel

Yes! Everything seems okay, and you can follow this path, but there is a problem again. The ceiling height in the room where the substrate was planned to be manufactured is insufficient to accommodate such a structure.

Then, I decided to mix the substrate by hand in a regular old bathroom. It's good that this was already available. We once bathed our children in it; now, it gave birth to a new mushroom life.

I decided to try first what it would look like. I tested my physical capabilities and determined how realistic and productive it would be.

At first, it was not easy. I had to exert a lot of physical effort. But then, I quickly became friends with this bathtub and a simple pitchfork, and mixing the substrate was even a pleasure.

I was sure we could start the season even with such a primitive kneading method. Well, that's great!!! We are already at the start! We are ready!!

While construction was underway, we studied the local market for raw materials for the substrate composition. My wife and I have enormous experience in this, and we knew well what raw materials were needed to ultimately obtain a suitable nutrient substrate.

The most convenient raw materials for us are fuel pellets and briquettes. In our region, many farmers have agricultural waste such as sunflower husks, straw, waste from the combine (polova/ukr), and waste from the wood processing industry (sawdust). The main thing is that in our region, within a radius of 31 mile, many small enterprises made fuel briquettes and pellets from all these raw materials. We entered contracts with these enterprises with little difficulty and began to import such raw materials constantly. Many people brought briquettes directly to our yard, which was very convenient.

Why was this particular raw material chosen? Firstly, it is easy to deliver and store. Since the raw materials were all compressed, there was no need for extensive storage facilities. Also, transporting 1t of straw pellets is different than bringing just a ton of such straw. It's like carrying the same amount of air along with the straw, and it's also necessary to cut it before use. In the case of briquettes, it was enough to weigh and pour the required number of pellets or braces into the bathtub, pour in the calculated amount of water, and mix several times. Briquettes and pellets quickly absorbed water, softened, and we received an excellent substrate consistency.

Then, all that remained was to pour this substrate into plastic bags and send it for sterilization.

A separate series of photographs shows our experiments with soaking briquettes and pellets from various raw materials. They show how, in a matter of minutes, a solid piece was transformed into an excellent loose substance with the necessary moisture, ready for use. The same thing happened when soaking raw materials in the bathroom.

CHAPTER 19

Experiments With Soaking Pellets and Briquettes

You can understand the essence of preparing a substrate based on fuel briquettes and pellets from the photographs.

That is how I bring briquettes in bags

Straw briquette

Filling with water

After 10 minutes

Raw materials are ready for use

Fuel pellets from agricultural waste

Pellets from a mixture of various herbs and grains

The raw materials are ready for use after soaking

We received excellent briquettes from Alder sawdust.

The particle size and structure were just right to produce shiitake substrate blocks.

Alder is also suitable for such types of mushrooms as Lion's mane mushroom and Reishi.

Next, in the photo, we see what this raw material looks like when soaked.

It is generally more difficult to find raw materials based on hardwood sawdust than agricultural waste in our area.

Sawdust briquettes

After soaking for 30 minutes, this is ready-made sawdust

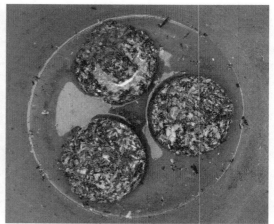

Sunflower husk briquettes

The raw materials are ready for use after soaking

Experiments have shown that the studied raw materials are easily moistened and acquire the necessary structure to manufacture substrate blocks.

All that remained was to analyze the raw materials for NPK and create substrate compositions for growing various types of mushrooms.

On the Amazon trading platform, many pellet granules with different compositions are available for sale. These include straw, wood, and a 50/50 wood/soy husk composition.

You can get significant discounts if you sign a contract for sufficient volumes.

CHAPTER 20

Substrate Manufacturing Process

After conducting experiments with soaking raw materials, we determined the optimal amount of water and time for soaking. We also sent samples to the laboratory to analyze the NPK content and calculate the substrate formula we needed for various types of mushrooms. Each component had its own soaking time, and we needed to organize the entire substrate production process accordingly.

After adding water, the briquette was soaked entirely for about 4 hours. If you use a mixer for these purposes, it will take no more than one hour.

I weighed the required pellets and briquettes in the morning and poured them into the bath. After this, I measured and poured the exact amount of water into the barrel with the addition of 3% gypsum. Then, I suddenly poured water onto the mixture of briquettes and pellets. It had to be done quickly to moisten all the dry ingredients. It's excellent when filling it with hot water, so the process happens faster. When the whole mixture was well soaked, I stirred it several times with a pitchfork, and the dry nutritional supplements were added. Then, a sample was taken to determine the humidity of the substrate and, if necessary, make corrections.

After the last mixing, the finished substrate was packaged in bags with a filter.

I loved taking the wet substrate in my hand, inhaling the aromas of the components that smelled like fields, bread, and grass.

We also made the bags by developing a unique technology that we are ready to share with readers. The main thing to note is that we could buy pre-made filter bags, but they cost about 50 cents each. Our packages cost only 5 cents, plus our labor; the savings were significant, considering we needed about 1,800 of these bags each month.

Savings in mushroom growing play an important role. By correctly calculating all costs, you can significantly reduce costs and, consequently, reduce production costs. In the following chapters, we will tell you how to do this.

Each substrate batch was identified, and all data was recorded in a log. It is worth noting that keeping a protocol indicating each batch's details is crucial. Adjustments can be made to the production cycle by analyzing the yield of each batch. It is an essential approach, and training yourself in this practice is good. In our journal, we recorded the batch number, substrate composition, substrate moisture, pH, weight, and number of blocks. Then, sowing data was added: sowing date, fungal culture, and strain.

We weighed each bag filled with the substrate, so all blocks weighed the same. To do this, we used an ordinary culinary scoop and scales. It took us less than an hour to fill 60-65 blocks. The block with the substrate was compacted by ordinary tapping on the table. The top of the bag was wrapped in an envelope, and the blocks were placed in the sterilizer. Then, it was plugged into the network, and you could go to rest. By morning, the substrate was ready.

I also loved to go out onto the porch late in the winter evening and inhale the aroma of the sterilizing substrate.

This smell spread throughout the yard. It was incredibly flavorful. Reminiscent of the scent of bread, grass, and caramel, this is a unique mushroom perfume for me.

At that moment, I realized that our business was developing, and each batch of smelling substrate was another step toward the intended goal.

Soaking pellets in the bath

The raw material is ready for use

Organic additives in bags: corn flour, wheat bran, and more

Wife Nadya pours substrate into bags. Granddaughter Lilya helps us

Measuring the acidity of the substrate

Placing blocks in the sterilizer

Sterilization area in operation

Steam outlet pipe at an angle of 45 degrees

Everything is ready for sowing (inoculation)

We quickly became involved in this work cycle, and the process unfolded like a piece of music – note by note. We entered the season on time, and work began to boil.

We produced the planned 100-110 kg (220-242lbs) of substrate every day. Plus, they have already begun to produce mycelium. To do this, we purchased a reliable and straightforward 50 Liter (13-gallon) autoclave sterilizer manufactured in the USSR, which did an excellent job with the assigned task. The grain for mycelium was sterilized at a pressure of about 0.1 MPa, which corresponded to 120°C (248°F). We will talk about this technology in further chapters.

Let's look at the critical points and details of preparing the substrate.

We receive raw materials with low humidity, around 5-7%. Pellets readily absorb water when soaked in such humidity. Knowing their initial moisture content, we can quite accurately calculate the required amount of water to obtain the final substrate moisture content we need. The process occurs quickly, thanks to the hygroscopicity of pellets and braces.

As a rule, the humidity of the substrate for mushrooms is 60-70%. Moreover, different mushroom cultures must know what humidity they prefer when growing them. For example, if oyster mushrooms prefer humidity in the 65-70% range, then shiitake mushrooms prefer no more than 62-63%. And sometimes, this is very important!

Therefore, determining the final moisture content of the substrate depends directly on the yield we ultimately get. Getting a good yield from a substrate such as oyster mushrooms with a low humidity of 58-60% is impossible! Very often, humidity plays a more significant role than nutritional value.

Therefore, at this stage, the mushroom grower needs to become familiar with this parameter and know how to control, maintain, and apply it.

Given the initial moisture content of the raw material (in our case, 5-7%), it is easy to calculate how much water needs to be added to achieve 70%.

CHAPTER 21

Determination of Substrate Moisture

There are two primary methods to measure humidity. One of them is expensive because it requires the purchase of a device such as an electronic humidity meter.

Its cost is in the range of 500-1000 dollars. But it is a very accurate and convenient device. Plus, it doesn't require attention. You need to load 5-20gramm (0.1-0.7 ounces) of the raw material under study into it and turn it on. It automatically measures humidity. In addition, it can store all data in memory or download it to a computer. Such devices are more suitable for large enterprises. Its operation is based on precisely weighing the substrate, which is then dried to a dry state by heating. Then, the processor makes the final calculation of the humidity.

Automatic electronic substrate moisture meter using drying method

I want to warn you not to be tempted to buy a moisture meter used for soil (see photo). These devices use an electrolytic method and are not accurate. They are unsuitable for our purposes, perhaps for express analysis of raw materials.

Such humidity meters are not suitable

Also, the method many consider correct will not work; this is squeezing the substrate in your hand until you get a few falling drops of water. Any drops of water are the so-called "unbound moisture," which should not be in the substrate. You must understand what the concept of "substrate moisture" means. The raw material must bind all moisture you introduce into the composition. That is, all moisture must be absorbed into the raw materials. Both concepts, "bound moisture" and "unbound moisture," speak for themselves.

The unbound moisture in the mushroom block accumulates in the lower part, leading to putrefactive processes. As a result, the block either dies entirely or has a meager yield.

Here at our home farm, we use a good, proven, and entirely accurate method of measuring humidity: a microwave oven.

Here, the principle is the same as that of the device described above.

We take the substrate under study, weigh it, and heat it in the microwave until all the moisture has evaporated. Then, we calculate the initial mass and dry residue.

For example, we took a sample of the raw material under study weighing 100g (3.5 ounces). We weigh with precise scales, accurate to 0,1g (0.003 ounces).

As it heats up, the substrate will lose moisture and weight., Stop drying and weigh the dry residue when the weight no longer decreases.

For example, before complete drying, the weight of the dry matter in the sample became 45g (1.5 ounces). That is, the weight has changed from the original 100g (3.5 ounces) to 35g . Then the initial humidity is 65%.

This process lasts, on average, 15-20 minutes.

It is strictly forbidden for the substrate to overheat and begin to char. Such a measurement will be invalid, and the whole process must start over. Therefore, to prevent this from happening, during the heating process, it is periodically necessary to remove the sample from the oven and actively mix it to prevent charring.

The whole process is detailed but necessary. In the future, if the starting raw material does not change, then there is no need to repeat this process before each substrate batch. Anyway, we periodically monitor the final moisture content of our substrate and record the data in the batch protocol.

As you can see, we devoted a significant part of the chapter to this process because it is crucial in production.

CHAPTER 22

Substrate Preparation and Composition

We have already learned how to measure the substrate's humidity. Now, let's start composing.

The substrate composition consists of a base and additives. The base is straw, husks, sawdust, or wood chips. Supplements are organic and mineral. The most common organic additive that increases the nitrogen content in the substrate, and therefore its productivity, is wheat bran. Corn flour, soybean, sunflower meal, or soy flour must be added to the bran for maximum substrate productivity. The total portion of nutritional supplements can range from 10 to 40% of the base weight.

It all depends on the mushroom culture. For example, to obtain high yields of King oyster mushrooms, Enoki, and Beech mushrooms, the substrate composition must contain up to 30-35% organic additives. For Oyster mushrooms, 20-25% is enough. For Shiitakes, additives should generally not exceed 10-15%.

The most common mineral additives are gypsum, chalk, and sometimes lime. Microelements such as magnesium, zinc, and manganese can also be used as salt compounds. We will not consider adding microelements to avoid complicating the initial perception. It is a more professional approach.

In future books, we will examine complex substrates' more profound calculations and composition, studying larger productions. We have already determined that different types of mushrooms require substrate formulas containing all the substances necessary for them.

The substrate composition for Shiitake, Lion's mane mushroom, and Reishi should be hardwood. The base can only be made from sawdust, but you can add 20-30% sunflower husks to save money or make components available.

However, to obtain high-quality mushrooms and a good harvest for shiitake, you need oak, beech, or alder sawdust. The taste and texture of mushrooms also depend on the type of wood used in the substrate. For example, mushrooms grown in alder have a mild flavor and texture similar to wild mushrooms, while oak gives Shiitake a spicy and springy texture when cooked.

For King oyster and Honey mushrooms, it is better to use softwood species, such as alder and poplar. Sunflower husks, cereal straws, corn cobs, and various nutritional supplements also work well. It affects the speed of substrate maturation and yield.

We will describe in detail the substrate formulas for each type of mushroom in the chapters dedicated to each mushroom separately.

All dry substrate components must be mixed. If you have a mixer, it will handle this easily. In our case, I poured all the ingredients into the bathtub and mixed everything with a pitchfork or shovel.

We wrote earlier that when mixing the substrate in the bathroom, as we did, you should not pour water in slowly. In this case, the pellets or briquettes will absorb water unevenly. The mixer does not have this problem.

Therefore, I poured the required amount of water into the barrel, which had previously been on dry raw materials in the bathroom. On average, I needed 57-59 liter (15-15.5 gallons) of water in our case. I immediately added gypsum to the water, mixed everything thoroughly, and suddenly poured all the water into the bathroom. Then, I left the pellets and briquettes to swell for 2-3 hours. After this time, I took a pitchfork and actively mixed this entire mixture until smooth. It took me about 10-15 minutes. We chose to work without a mixer for the reasons described above. It was our choice, but everyone could go their way here.

Of course, using a mixer for this process would be more efficient.

*Pour gypsum into a barrel of water and mix it for uniform application.
Then, quickly pouring water onto the briquettes*

When the substrate composition was well prepared and mixed, we measured its moisture content again, if necessary. If everything suited us, we would start filling the bags with this mixture.

Nadya poured the substrate into bags, weighed it, brought it to the required weight (1,5 kg), and handed it to me. I compacted it, wrapped the free end in an envelope, and placed such blocks in the sterilizer.

This method of laying the blocks in the sterilizer avoided entering outside air into the block and its contamination when transferred to a clean area. This straightforward and reliable method has proven itself well and has not caused malfunctions.

As I wrote earlier, the sterilizer included about 65 such blocks. After filling the sterilizer barrel, I closed the lid and turned it on for heating.

The whole process of stuffing and folding blocks into the sterilizer took 45-50 minutes.

Next, clean workplaces and fill out a work log.

After 3-4 hours, the barrel heated up and released steam with a slight hiss. The sterilization process began. I averaged 8-10 hours of exposure time, which was monitored by a timer.

The smell of the substrate spread throughout the yard, and as I wrote earlier, it was incredibly addictive.

Different components in the substrate also gave off a distinct smell. I am sure that if anyone loves this smell at this stage, they will love mushroom growing.

So, I wrote that we prepared the substrate in the evening so it would be sterilized by the morning after heat treatment. That is, our working day ended with turning on the sterilizer.

The timer turned off the sterilization in the morning, and the blocks cooled. The substrate will cool in the barrel for another day, and we will take it out after it has cooled. But we will inoculate the substrate, which we sterilized the day before yesterday and in the afternoon. It will have cooled down enough in the clean room by this time.

The continuous substrate production process consists of the cyclic nature of mixing, sterilization, cooling, and inoculation. As a result, you will produce a ready-made substrate, which you will send for incubation every day.

You will probably be able to plan these cycles correctly. We have described the main point here.

CHAPTER 23

Inoculation of Substrate Blocks

The next stage is the inoculation of blocks with mycelium.

Our block production cycle had the following sequence: the process was completed in one sterilizer in the morning, and the blocks rested and cooled there. In the second sterilizer, the blocks had already cooled sufficiently, although they still had a temperature of about +70°C (158°F) and were awaiting further processing. We transfer them to a clean area for cooling. We unloaded the third sterilizer into the clean room yesterday, and the blocks will be inoculated today. The vacated sterilizer will be loaded with new blocks today.

In the meantime, in the clean room, cooled blocks were already brought in yesterday. We seed these blocks with mycelium.

Inoculation is the introduction of fungal mycelium into a sterile substrate.

Fungal mycelium is a sprouted fungal culture on a carrier added to the substrate. The type of carrier determines the kind of mycelium. A culture grown on a liquid nutrient medium is called liquid mycelium, on grain – grain mycelium, on substrate – substrate mycelium, and on specially prepared wood sticks –stick mycelium.

Each type of mycelium has characteristics that allow it to be introduced and worked with. The most common type of mycelium is grain mycelium, which we chose for our work. In our practice, we also worked with mycelium of all kinds. Liquid mycelium requires special equipment and application skills for its production and sowing. Working with them is often chosen at large enterprises, where the appropriate technology was initially selected.

Substrate mycelium is suitable for forming certain types of substrate blocks in long bars and does not have a breathing filter. In this case, it is also necessary to initially select a production technology and build the entire technological process, considering such blocks.

Our book will examine two types of mycelium: rod and grain. We experimented with rod mycelium and will share the results with you. We value the creative process in our work and love to experiment and improve our knowledge and skills.

The chapter devoted to this topic will discuss mycelium in more detail. Now, let's get back to working in the clean room.

The clean room (inoculation room) is the heart of the enterprise, and its proper operation depends on defects in substrate blocks. We encountered a situation where, at another enterprise where we previously worked, employees' failure to comply with the rules of work in the inoculation room and sanitary standards led to the defect of a significant part of the batch.

The work's success depends on compliance with all rules and regulations for disinfecting the premises and maintaining its cleanliness. Unique clothing is required to work in the inoculation room: a robe or overalls designed exclusively for work in this room and slippers that will be disinfected after each use. All exposed areas of the body must be clean, hair must be protected, the face must be covered with a mask, and hands must be protected with gloves that are periodically disinfected during work.

Before starting work, the clean room is treated with an ultraviolet lamp for 60 minutes, then the fresh air supply is turned on for ventilation, and after 30-40 minutes, work can begin. Before entering the inoculation room, wear unique clothing, treat your hands with 70% ethyl alcohol for quick disinfection, and then move on to the inoculation room.

All tools used in the work (a spoon for adding mycelium, scissors for cutting a bag with mycelium, a soldering iron for sealing bags), the inoculation table, and the curtains of the laminar flow hood are pre-treated with alcohol. All work is carried out in the laminar flow hood area; taking the open substrate bag outside the curtains is not recommended.

The grain mycelium must be loose by being kneaded in a bag before starting work, then treated with alcohol and brought into the planting area. The top of the bag with the mycelium must be cut off, and the spoon used for dosing the grain mycelium added to the substrate must be disinfected.

Next, you should take each block one by one, unfold the edges of the film, add 1-2 spoons of planting mycelium to it, and mix the mycelium with the substrate. The bag should then be sealed and set aside.

Many sources on planting mycelium recommend simply pouring the mycelium on top of the substrate and then sealing the bag with a hot-soldering iron. However, this method has many disadvantages. The block with the substrate begins to overgrow slowly and unevenly, starting from the top.

The substrate in such a block is dense, which leads to low air permeability. Often, the block is not yet entirely colonized by mycelium, but the mushrooms are already beginning to grow outward. The development and productivity of such blocks could be higher. We have wholly abandoned such a system.

After many experiments, we have developed a very effective and simple technology. After pouring a portion of mycelium onto the surface of the substrate, we knead the substrate with active movements of the fingers, pressing on the side walls of the bag. Currently, the substrate is loosened, making it more aerated, and the mycelium grains are mixed almost evenly with the entire substrate mass. Such manipulations make it possible to obtain a well-breathing substrate with a uniform distribution of mycelial grains, facilitating rapid and uniform colonization of the block by mycelium, the so-called growth points. Thanks to this, the block was mastered by mycelium much faster and evenly.

It was the key to a successful harvest.

Sowing blocks is Nadiia's area of responsibility

After sealing, the block is no longer in danger. Breathable air enters it only through a HEPA filter, and now it can be safely transferred to the incubator.

After inoculation is completed, all blocks must be marked with the date of sowing, the name of the crop, and, if necessary, the strain.

The entire batch of 65 blocks was usually sown within 2 hours from the start of preparation. Now, Nadya handed these blocks to me through the intermediate corridor. I put them in a vegetable box and took them to the incubator. There, our blocks began a new life.

It's like a child who was born in pain (in labor) is now put into a cozy cradle, where special conditions are created for his growth and development.

Hmm... the comparison was born as an impromptu, but I liked this analogy.

Next, the clean room is cleaned and prepared to receive blocks from the sterilizer for the next sowing.

After the sowing, transferring a new batch of blocks from the sterilizer to the inoculation room immediately begins.

I am near the sterilizers currently. We open the transfer window gateway. Because a relatively intense excess pressure is maintained in the clean room, when the airlock is opened, clean filtered air comes out of it towards the sterilizer. It creates a situation in which dirty air cannot enter the inoculation room because it is not allowed in by the overpressure flow from the airlock.

While in this stream, I open the lid of the sterilizer barrel. Inside are sterilized blocks, which I quickly transfer through the airlock to the inoculation room. Nadya puts them on the prepared table for further cooling.

Upon completion of work, the clean room is cleaned. The floor is washed with detergents, all surfaces are treated with disinfectant solutions and alcohol, the bactericidal lamp is turned on, everything is closed, and the lights are turned off.

Very important! After finishing work, the fresh, purified air fan **does not turn off**! Otherwise, dirty air may enter the room through various cracks. Instead of turning it off, the fan speed is reduced to 5% of the total power. It is enough to create a slight but excess pressure in the room. Excess pressure is observed by gravity valves built into various areas of the room. At this time, the valves themselves move slightly.

Now you can start other work on the farm.

CHAPTER 24

Mycelium

In the previous chapter, we looked at the different types of seed mycelium used for sowing substrate blocks, differing depending on the medium on which the vegetative culture of the fungus grew.

A fungal culture germinating on a nutrient medium in a test tube will be needed to obtain working mycelium.

All types of mycelium are available on the Internet and in specialized stores. Such mycelium is often called mother mycelium, and special laboratory conditions are required to work with it. When reseeding from a test tube, the mycelium is replicated and stored in the refrigerator (replication is the process of reproduction).

The next step in mycelium production is to create a fungal interculture. To do this, a small part of the mycelium, germinated on a nutrient medium, is transplanted onto grain in a glass jar with a volume of 500-700 gram (1-1.5lb) for germination. Mycelium germination on grain occurs in a thermostat, a unique cabinet with the necessary microclimate for optimal mycelium development. The process lasts at a temperature of +24°C (75°F) for up to 30 days, depending on the volume of grain into which fouling occurs. When the mycelium entirely masters the grain, it can be transplanted onto the working mycelium in a larger volume. From one 500 gram (1.1-lb) jar, you can get up to 20kg (44 pounds) of working mycelium, which is then planted on the substrate.

Today, obtaining a cover crop has become much more manageable. On sites like Amazon Marketplace, you can purchase syringes from liquid cultures of various types of mushrooms. It opens up the possibility of inoculating sterilized grain with liquid mycelium from a syringe and obtaining an intermediate culture immediately.

This method simplifies the process and reduces the time required to obtain a catch crop. Even novice mushroom growers can use this method to quickly and efficiently obtain mycelium for further production of substrate blocks.

The entire inoculation occurs by pouring a liquid mycelium culture into a sterilized grain and mixing thoroughly.

It is necessary to store mycelium cultures in the refrigerator in clean laboratory conditions to exclude the possibility of infection and, consequently, loss of the fungal culture.

In our practice, we preferred grain mycelium because of its versatility and ease of use. Instead of creating our laboratory for growing mycelium from test tubes and Petri dishes, we preferred to purchase ready-made grain mycelium from specialized laboratories.

In conditions where only the two of us worked on the farm, we would have needed more time to propagate mycelium through pure cultures from a test tube.

In Ukraine, a sufficient number of laboratories specialize in producing working grain mycelium, and we have collaborated with many of them. It allowed us to purchase mycelium in the needed quantities and use it to sow sterilized blocks directly.

Working mycelium from the manufacturer. Weight 6kg

Later, we purchased an autoclave and began producing mycelium from an intermediate culture that we also purchased from our colleagues. This method also allowed us to replicate the working mycelium to suit our needs.

Autoclave KVU-50

We advise everyone who builds a similar business to first focus on purchasing ready-made mycelium. There are pretty good laboratories in Europe and the USA, such as Amycel, Sylvan, and Mycelia.

However, we will still tell you about the technology for replicating mycelium for your home farm needs.

CHAPTER 25

Preparing Grain For Mycelium

First, you need to purchase and prepare grain.

In our case, the most affordable grain is barley.

Oats also work well for this. But oats are rare in our area, so we used barley.

There are two options for preparing grain for mycelium. Both methods aim to moisten the grain to a moisture content of 50%.

The first method is cold.

The grain is first poured into polypropylene bags and washed with running water. After washing, the grain is placed in any container and filled with cold water. If the temperature in the room where the soaking process occurs is +10-20°C (50-68°F), the grain can reach the required humidity in 10-12 hours. If the process occurs in the summer at a temperature of +20-30°C (68-86°F), the time can be halved. However, there is a risk of grain fermentation. Replacing the water with fresh two or three times is necessary to prevent the grain from fermenting.

The second method is hot.

It involves heating and preparing the already washed grain in a water bath. The grain is placed in water-filled bags, and the electric heater is turned on. The water temperature is brought to +80-85°C (176-185°F). This method allows you to cook grain in 2-3 hours.

However, it is vital to control the process to avoid overcooking the grain, which could render it unusable. Therefore, it is necessary to carry out moisture control measurements or check the condition of the grain.

The water must drain well after removing the grain bags from the barrel. It may take about an hour.

After preparation, the grain is poured into the bath, adding up to 1% gypsum. Then, it is thoroughly mixed and packaged in bags for subsequent sterilization.

Use polypropylene bags as they can withstand steam sterilization temperatures of +120°C (248°F).

Such bags are found on USA, China, and Europe trading platforms.

Bags of grain for mycelium must be sealed before sterilization.

The sterilization mode is +120°C (248F) at a pressure of 0.1 MPa for 3-4 hours.

CHAPTER 26

Inoculation of Grain Mycelium

After sterilization, the grain is inoculated in the same way as the substrate blocks. The bags are sealed and mixed thoroughly so that the mycelium is evenly spread throughout the volume.

We packed the grain in 2kg (4lb) bags to make it easy to work with small batches of the substrate. The main thing is to ensure that about 50% of the volume of free space remains in the bag so that the grain can be mixed after sowing.

Remember to monitor the process of mycelium overgrowth in the incubator, which usually takes about 15 days.

The grain mycelium in the incubator develops very quickly, generating heat, so it is necessary to monitor the temperature in the center of the bag. It should not exceed +28°C (82°F), and the temperature in the incubator should be within +22-24°C (72-75°F).

The temperature in the center of the block is affected by the percentage of royal mycelium introduced. The higher the application rate, the more intense the ripening process, and the higher the temperature correspondingly.

If the rate of introduced mother culture is 5%, then the incubation period will be 14-15 days.

For example, when applied in a 1-2% volume, the overgrowing time will lengthen up to 20-30 days.

Ensure the bags with mycelium in the box do not touch each other. Overheating will occur, the mycelium will die, and only dry grain will remain. In general, such mycelium can be used for sowing, but it is better not to allow this.

After the end of the incubation period, the mycelium must be used for sowing substrate blocks or transferred to the refrigerator for further storage.

At a refrigerator temperature of +2-4°C (36-39°F), the mycelium retains its properties for 3-4 months.

Pay attention to the bags during incubation.

If condensation appears inside the bag, this usually indicates that the entire unit is infected. Observe such bags and remove them from the incubator in time.

Plan the purchase and production of mycelium to avoid gaps in the production process.

By following these steps and ensuring the necessary sterility and quality control, you can create an effective mycelium replication process for your mushroom production.

Pouring the prepared grain into bags

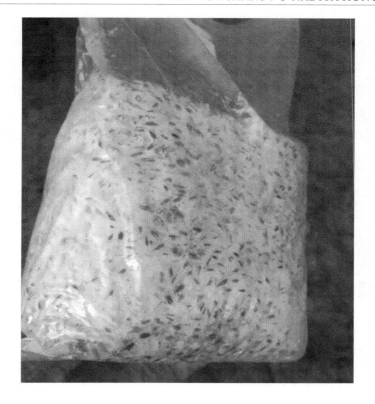

Ready mycelium in 12-14 days

Ready mycelium stored in the refrigerator

A case of mycelium overheating when the bags touch the side walls

CHAPTER 27

Mycelium on Sticks

Another variety of mycelium is rod-shaped. The carrier is made of wooden sticks infected with a fungal culture. Previously, and even today, many Chinese enterprises still work with such mycelium.

We also used this variety on our farm and in other industries.

What advantages does it have over the grain?

Firstly, it is very inexpensive to manufacture.

Secondly, it is more adaptive than grain, improving the overall picture of block ripening.

Thirdly, they are effortless to inoculate.

These are the main advantages.

We tried using different sticks for this technology. One of the first experiments was Chinese skewers "chushu" ("bamboo skewers" or "bamboo sticks" in English).

They were easy to use and quickly entered the substrate with their sharp end. But, since their contact area was insignificant, it was necessary to inoculate one block with two or three such sticks.

In the end, the experiment with shiitake culture showed promising results.

The essence of the technology is simple.

The sticks are pre-soaked in boiling water with 1% sugar. After cooling, they are packaged in bags with a filter, like grain mycelium. You still need to add a little substrate or soaked grain to the sticks in the bag.

They are then sterilized in the usual way.

After sterilization, the bag`s contents are inoculated with either a pure culture of their Petri dish or an intermediate master culture on the grain.

After 15-20 days, we will get mycelium ready.

All details can be seen in step-by-step photos.

Soaking and welding sticks in a 1% sugar solution

Adding sawdust to the bag

Sterilizing rods in a pressure cooker

Mycelium on sticks ready for use

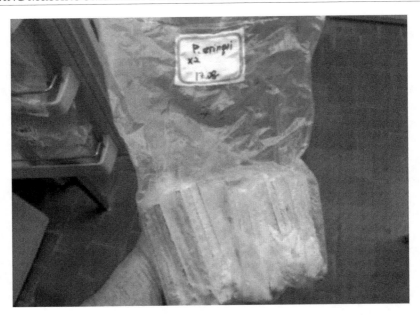

Then, we found a supplier of square rods with a cross-section of 6x6 mm (0.2x0.2 inches), used to produce cotton candy. It was the best option, both in price and availability. The main thing is to ensure that the order is not made from coniferous wood. Beech and alder were best suited for this.

But in the end, we had a stable and reliable supply of grain mycelium, so we still used more of it on our farm. However, it was always planned to switch to a rod.

CHAPTER 28

Block Incubation

What kind of climate is needed in the incubator?

First, the blocks that enter the incubator warm up gradually. Peak warming occurs on days 7-20. This process is excepted. However, it must be controlled and responded to in critical situations. The maximum temperature in the center of the block should not exceed +29°C (84°F).

At higher temperatures, mushroom mycelium may die. For mushroom crops such as shiitake and enoki, it is recommended that temperatures not exceed +27°C (80°F) be allowed.

Therefore, unlike in growing chambers, in an incubator, we do not pay so much attention to the temperature in the room but the temperature in the blocks.

If the block's temperature rises above the established threshold, measures must be taken to reduce it. It can be achieved by using a ventilation system with adjustable valves or other methods of regulating the heat in the incubator.

It is also vital to ensure adequate humidity in the incubator, as mushroom mycelium requires a specific humidity level to thrive. Regularly monitoring moisture and, if necessary, moistening the blocks in the incubator will help maintain optimal conditions for mushroom growth.

Therefore, controlling temperature and humidity in the incubator is crucial to successful mushroom cultivation and requires systematic monitoring and regulation.

But, often, it is enough not to turn on the cooling but to increase the performance of the recirculation fans. It must be done to ensure thermal removal from the surface of the blocks. Therefore, the intensity of air mixing in the incubator is significant.

Sometimes, mobile axial fans, which can be locally directed to the heating batches of the substrate, work well in this case.

It is unacceptable to cool with cold air suddenly, and even more so, letting in cold air from the street.

It can lead to condensation under the film and the death of the blocks. Already mature blocks will react to cold air as an induction to fruiting, and the mushrooms will begin to grow (shoot) directly under the film in the incubator. Therefore, enhanced recirculation is in the incubator.

The incubator's light must be turned on only during loading and unloading operations. As in growing rooms, the CO_2 level is not controlled because the upper limit can be 5000 ppm. However, humidity must be maintained within 70-80%.

It is necessary to ensure that the blocks do not release internal moisture from the block into the room. This process is called a "humidity gradient." If you do not consider this point, the blocks will lose some substrate moisture during incubation. As we said earlier, the humidity of the substrate directly affects the yield. Therefore, the loss of moisture in the blocks during incubation equals the loss of yield.

Affordable low-pressure nozzles, such as greenhouse foggers, can maintain humidity levels in the incubator. It is okay if some drops fall on the blocks, as they easily tolerate this. Due to the damp mist on the floor, the humidity in the chamber is further increased.

It is also crucial to protect the substrate from mice and rats. If you don't take appropriate measures, they will appear. We used an effective combination of insecticides, traps, and special glue.

The glue worked incredibly well for this. However, the best results are achieved with an integrated approach. Remember this because rodents can cause severe damage to your blocks.

So, in the incubator, we do not control CO_2, maintain humidity, control the temperature in the center of the control blocks, provide airflow, do not turn on the light, and... catch mice.

Knowing the incubation time of each crop, you must correctly plan the release of the substrate so that you can ensure a continuous conveyor of fruiting of the planned crops. After all, our mushrooms are already waiting everywhere, in stores and restaurants, so our supplies must be stable and continuous.

I have always enjoyed watching the mycelium grow in blocks in different batches. Every day, I found time to go into the incubator and not only measure and adjust the temperature and humidity. I loved seeing how life changed in the blocks. The mycelium increasingly occupies dark areas of the substrate and actively moves throughout the block. I especially enjoyed watching the Shiitake blocks incubate. They are the most unique of all mushrooms. However, I will talk about this in chapters that touch on the description of all crops and the features of their cultivation.

I'll share how we saved a lot on shelves for the incubator. We saved on their complete absence in the incubator as such.

Instead of shelves, we used black citrus vegetable boxes. We purchased them in advance at a meager price, about 10 cents apiece.

We put blocks in these boxes and stacked them one on top of the other at the height that the incubator allows.

Thus, we did not have to install expensive shelves, and the density of loading the incubator with blocks was very high.

However, this situation required special attention to internal ventilation. With such a loading density, we had to ensure air movement throughout the entire volume of improvised shelves made from boxes. As I wrote earlier, this is a critical condition.

Further, if four blocks were placed in a box, their sides would touch. That could have caused more heating than if they had not touched. In the winter, this could save costs on heating the incubator and, therefore, on energy resources. In summer, this could lead to overheating of the blocks. All this must be considered, and appropriate decisions must be made.

It is unacceptable for shiitake blocks in boxes to touch each other. They absolutely cannot stand such a neighborhood. In places where the blocks touch, the characteristic popcorn will not form; accordingly, these areas will not bear fruit. This is a characteristic of shiitake. Therefore, for high-quality incubation, we placed only 2 shiitake blocks in a box so that the distance between the blocks is at least 1cm (0.3 inches).

Vegetable boxes for the incubator have arrived

Work in the incubator

Substrate blocks for incubation in boxes

Blocks should not touch each other

Ripe substrate block

Now, we have an incubator with blocks of different ages maturing in it. The time has come for the incubation of some batches to expire. Many blocks have already matured and want to produce offspring in the form of mushroom-fruiting bodies. And that means it's time for us to move to the cultivation premises.

CHAPTER 29

Cultivation

Your excitement and joy should be indescribable when the moment of cultivation arrives. The first substrate blocks grown by your labor are placed on the shelves of the growing chambers. You are already anticipating the moment when the long-awaited mushrooms, such as you saw from the authors of this book, will appear on these shelves, as if in a forest clearing. They will delight you with their charm and diversity.

Soon, you will see your first pets on the shelves of growing chambers. It's fantastic to see such a variety of beautiful mushrooms, inhale their delicate aroma, pick up blocks on which your pets grow in heaps, and wink at you.

It's exhilarating to walk into a chamber early in the morning and see the notable difference between what you saw last night and today. Yesterday, they were small peas, but today, they are real mushrooms.

After two to three hours, they are ready to gather.

Yes, the autumn atmosphere you created in your pets` cells does its job. Mushrooms, feel comfortable in this climate. Thank you for your harvest.

According to natural laws, they only strive to leave offspring and not to get into your frying pan. But that is another story.

By the way, in the dark, under the light of a flashlight, you can see how mushrooms emit a mist of spores, which are their reproductive organs. It looks like the mushrooms are being smoked. It's simply amazing. That's the beauty of the mushroom business — it is profitable and beautiful.

And now, we come to another critical stage — cultivation.

Here, we face a lot of different subtleties and details.

Mushrooms cannot grow as they do in the forest. Each crop must create its conditions for growth and maturation. Things get even more complicated when different cultures are in the same chamber.

But this is interesting!

We will introduce you to the most exciting stage in this business — cultivation in a growth chamber.

We have three growing chambers, so it is advisable to place mushrooms that need a similar climate in one chamber. For example, more thermophilic but tolerant to high carbon dioxide content mushrooms, such as Shiitake and Poplar mushrooms, can be placed in one chamber.

Cold-loving species such as Enoki (winter honey agaric), Shimeji (white and beech), and Nameko, which also tolerate high humidity and carbon dioxide, can be grown in another chamber.

It is better to grow Oyster mushrooms and Pulmonaris in a separate chamber. These need moderate humidity, good airflow, and no more than 900-1000 ppm carbon dioxide content.

In the chapters where we describe different mushroom cultures, we will look in more detail at the subtle climate parameters characteristic of each species. These differences in climate preferences between different crops must be considered for convenient and correct planning of sowing schedules. Nadya is undoubtedly a great specialist in this matter. She has a unique talent to see far ahead and present a picture of the world in mushroom production. She was always entrusted with correct production planning at all the enterprises where we worked and successfully coped with it. Therefore, this task was also her responsibility on our home farm, and she handled it to a high standard.

Having gained some experience, you will also gain an understanding of this subtle matter. The main thing is to learn to record all your actions in logs and protocols.

Then, you can always analyze, adjust your actions, and learn how to plan production effectively.

CHAPTER 30

Overview of Cultures and Strains

Now, let's look at the features of cultivating each mushroom culture we grew on our farm. Of course, it is unlikely that in the format of this book, it will be possible to describe all our experiences in these cultures sufficiently. It is simply a considerable amount of information and deep practical experience of our knowledge. Moreover, we are already working on a separate book, where we will devote as much of our experience working with them to each culture as possible.

CHAPTER 31

Shiitake (Lentinula Edodes), Chestnut Mushroom, Sleeping Buddha Mushroom

In China, Shiitake mushrooms are called the Imperial mushroom. According to legend, only members of the imperial family could eat them.

Shiitake, one of the first in a series of exotic mushrooms, conquered the market of Ukraine and Europe. My wife and I worked at an experimental enterprise in Kyiv, where we first began cultivating this mushroom. There, we devoted almost 10 years to this mushroom. We collected information about it, piece by piece. Using our experience, we developed the technology and promoted sales of this mushroom in Ukrainian networks. Over time, the consumer fell in love with this mushroom. By this time, we had already worked out the technology, gained sufficient experience, and continued to grow it at other enterprises.

The nutritional and medicinal value of Shiitake is the most studied among cultivated mushrooms.

Fruiting bodies contain a high content of phosphorus, calcium, and iron. B vitamins: B1, B2, B3, provitamin D-2.

Shiitake fruiting bodies contain a water-soluble fraction of lignin. A unique polysaccharide, leutinan, with high therapeutic potential has also been identified.

Thanks to their immunomodulatory and anticancer properties, Shiitake mushrooms and their products benefit human health.

The polysaccharide Leuthinan is widely used in AIDS treatment protocols. It has a bactericidal effect on Staphylococcus aureus and Escherichia coli, and its hypoglycemic impact is manifested in reducing blood cholesterol levels.

Growing technology

To make a Shiitake substrate, a prerequisite is the presence of wood in the substrate formula, which is from 50 to 90%. Usually, they use oak, beech, and alder; you can add sunflower or buckwheat husks, bran, corn, and soy flour. A high calcium content is essential for Shiitake, so chalk or gypsum is added.

Optimal indicators for Shiitake substrate are substrate humidity of 58-61%, pH 5.6, total nitrogen content of 0.8-1%, and C/N ratio of 50-70/1.

Add mycelium to the substrate at a rate of 3 to 7% and mix thoroughly. The substrate's density is 0.7, so it must be well aerated.

We used the following substrate formula on our farm:

Option #1

Briquettes or pellets from alder sawdust – 50%

Wheat straw pellets or briquettes – 15%

Sunflower husk briquettes – 20%

Wheat bran – 15%

Gypsum – 1%

Option #2

Briquettes or pellets of oak, beech, or alder – 80%

Corn flour – 10%

Wheat bran – 10%

Gypsum – 1%

Important condition! The density of shiitake blocks should be no more than 0,6-0,7 g/cm3 (0.021-0.025 lb/in^3).

It is essential for Shiitake since this mushroom is very demanding during incubation on good substrate aeration.

Calculated by the formula **$\rho=m/V$**

Shiitake mushrooms have the most extended incubation period compared to other mushroom cultures. Depending on the strain, it is 90-120 days. During incubation, the blocks go through unique stages.

The first stage involves colonizing the substrate with mycelium, lasting 14-20 days. During this time, the substrate becomes white and enters the second stage – maturation. The ripening or "popcorn" stage lasts 30 days and consists of the formation of tubercles on the surface of the substrate, which resemble popcorn in shape.

The third stage is pigmentation. The surface of the block acquires a dark brown color, and a dense protective layer is formed on the surface of which the rudiments of mushrooms will form.

When the block is wholly pigmented, it is transferred from the incubator to the growing chamber for germination.

There is also a unique property of Shiitake substrate blocks. For example, the blocks are fully ripe by the 120th day and are ready to begin bearing fruit. But, for some reason (the season is not ready yet, there are no orders, or the blocks are waiting to be sent to the buyer), there is no way to put them up for fruiting. So, Shiitake blocks will do quite well resting in the incubator and waiting for their finest hour. And nothing will happen to

them, even if we keep them for another 30-50 days. The main thing at that time was not to disturb them, monitor the stability of the temperature, and maintain humidity in the chamber so that they did not dry out. Only Shiitake blocks have this feature. Blocks of other crops, in this case, would have to be transferred to the refrigerator for storage, which, of course, is very expensive.

At one enterprise where we worked as technologists, at the startup stage, it was impossible to expose the blocks

from the incubator to fruiting for three months after they had ripened. Although they lost a quarter of their weight, they were still exposed to the fruiting chambers, and in the end, an excellent result was obtained. As a result, these blocks lived in the incubator for seven months.

In the growing chamber on shelves, blocks are placed at a distance of 150 - 200 mm (6-8 inches) for free formation of fruiting bodies over the entire surface of the block. Therefore, blocks weigh up to 3kg (6.6 pounds) for convenience when picking mushrooms.

When picking mushrooms, such a block is convenient to hold in your hand and cut mushrooms.

Mushrooms are harvested at the stage of technical maturity when the mushroom cap is detached from the stem. Shiitake mushrooms are the least demanding of the climate. Ready, mature blocks are quickly initiated immediately after removing the film and begin to bear fruit. An extensive range of climate parameters is suitable for mushroom growth.

They grow equally well in temperatures ranging from +14°C to 24°C (57 to 75°F) and with humidity from 80 to 95%. They also have a relatively high tolerance to CO_2 levels and grow successfully even at 2000 ppm.

So, in general, this is a virtually problem-free cultivated mushroom. In addition, it has almost no pests or diseases.

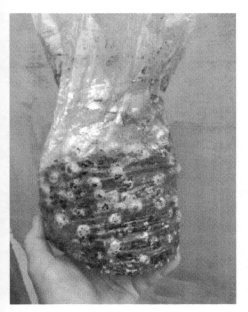

Out of all the variety of Shiitake strains, we settled on two – M3782 and M3790. These are entirely different strains, and you need to know the intricacies of their cultivation. For example, M3790 can immediately deliver the entire yield in the first wave, reaching 22-25%. And M3782 has a more extended fruiting period, and you can harvest up to 5 waves on it and ultimately get up to 50-70% of the yield. Then, the technological process must include soaking these blocks between waves in special containers.

At our home farm, we settled on the M3790. It has another feature that we have used successfully on our farm. If the blocks are placed from the incubator into the fruiting chamber, and the film is not removed immediately, then small peas – primordia – will begin to form under the film. And the longer the block stands with the film, the more primordia are tied under the film. So, by adjusting the moment of opening the film, we can regulate the number of mushrooms on the surface of the block.

That directly affects the size and quality of mushrooms.

The photo shows the conditions of the mushrooms we received. It is the size that suits our consumers. As for the yield, we have long learned to consistently get up to 25% in the first wave.

This strain also has one unique feature.

If the incubation time is short, the blocks must be perforated at the white block stage before the formation of popcorn. That is, the surface of the block must be pierced. The blocks begin to breathe more intensely, become pigmented faster, and can be put up for initiation on the 45th day.

At this stage, the block is not entirely brown but can already yield about 15% of the harvest in the first wave.

After harvesting, it is necessary to soak the blocks for 4 hours and again put them out for fruiting for the second wave. By this time, the block will already have a more intense brown color and may give another 10% of the second wave. As a result, for an entire cycle, in two waves, we will get almost the same harvest if we force the block to bear fruit in the first wave after 120 days. But we got the first harvest much earlier, although not the maximum.

This technique justifies itself when a large order suddenly arrives, but there needs to be more ready-made mature blocks. The M3790 strain reveals its maximum potential if incubated for 114-120 days.

Shiitake blocks can bear fruit in up to five waves. After each fruiting period, the blocks are hydrogenated for additional hydration and leached for metabolic production.

This process can be done in two ways: soaking the blocks in a water container or using unique mechanisms to hydrate them. It is labor-intensive but highly efficient.

After harvesting, mushrooms must be quickly cooled to 0,5°C - 2°C (33-35F). That is the key to their quality during storage. It is advisable to package or cover the mushrooms to retain moisture. Under such conditions, mushrooms can be stored for up to 30 days.

The yield of Shiitake is high: from 300 to 500g (2.2 pounds) of substrate to 1kg (10.5-17.6 ounces) of fresh mushrooms. If the substrate formula and growing conditions are balanced, biological efficiency ranges from 80% to 190%.

With its nutritional and medicinal properties and unique taste, Shiitake fully confirms its name, "IMPERIAL MUSHROOM." Unpretentiousness to external influences and long shelf life make this mushroom one of the most popular in industrial cultivation. Shiitake also has high culinary qualities. This mushroom is used in sauces and soups. They are fried and marinated, and the cap can be stuffed. If Shiitake is added to meat and fish dishes, the latter's taste is revealed, and the dishes acquire uniqueness and originality. They cook quickly, in 3-5 minutes, and become soft, tender, and buttery; this attracts gourmets.

CHAPTER 32

Flammulina Velutipes (Curtis) Singer Winter Mushroom, Futu, Velvet Shank, "Seafood Mushrooms" or Enoki (Enokitake)

The name Winter honey fungus speaks for itself, determining the appropriate climate requirements for its cultivation.

The fruiting bodies of Honey mushrooms contain polysaccharides, bioactive endopolysaccharides, and protein. B vitamins: B1, B2, folic acid, vitamin PP.

Even in ancient times, Chinese residents used Flammulina to prevent cancer, liver and kidney diseases, and lower blood pressure.

A unique protein (FIP-five-fungal immunomodulatory protein) has been identified in the fruiting bodies of Flammulina, which stimulates the activity of peripheral lymphocytes. Enoki contains ergothioneine, an amino acid with high functional value.

It has been proven that the structure of polysaccharides and molecules of protein-glucan complexes in mushrooms have a high adsorbing property, removing the remains of toxins, heavy metals, and radionuclides.

Growing technology

The original pleasant taste and relatively simple cultivation technology open the active introduction of Winter honey mushrooms into industrial cultivation. In China, mushrooms are very popular and grown by about 25 million farmers.

Flammulina ranks third in popularity after Shiitake and Oyster mushrooms.

Honey fungus is cultivated on various agricultural wastes, such as grain straw, sunflower husks, and wood.

Optimal substrate parameters for growing Winter honey fungus: substrate humidity 63-68%; pH 6.5-7.5; nitrogen content 1.0-1.5%; C/N ratio 30-50/1; density 500-600 kg/m³ (31-37lb/ft³).

We used the following composition:

Straw pellets – 30%

Sunflower husk pellets – 30%

Corn flour – 10%

Wheat bran – 20%

Soy flour – 10%

Gypsum – 1%

The application rate of planting mycelium is 2.5 to 5% of the substrate weight.

To grow fruiting bodies, use a small substrate volume in a bag to speed up incubation and form a long stalk for fruiting.

Incubation period: 21-30 days.

Incubation temperature: +20-21°C (68-71°F)

Humidity: 90-95%

During incubation, the temperature must be strictly controlled so as not to destroy the entire batch. Mycelium does not tolerate even slight overheating.

To initiate the primordia formation, cut off the top of the bag at a height of 20 cm and lower the temperature to +4-10°C (39-50°F). The humidity in the chamber should be 95-99%, CO_2 0.2-0.4%, and lighting 20-50 lux.

After 5-7 days, beads of mushroom primordia will appear. The temperature in the chamber will be increased to +10-15°C (50-60°F), with humidity at 90-95%. After 7-10 days, you can harvest the mushroom. Harvesting the mushroom is as easy as possible; you need to remove the entire clump from the substrate immediately.

Flammulina is stored and packaged together with substrate particles without cutting. Mushrooms are kept in the refrigerator at a temperature of +0.5-1°C (33-35°F) for 14-20 days.

The yield, subject to all technological standards, is high, from 200 to 600g (17 to 21.1 ounces) per 1 kg (2.2 pounds) of substrate in two waves.

Enoki has unique taste properties and has many admirers around the world. Their long stem and small cap resemble mushroom noodles and have a crunchy texture.

The unique caramel aroma of Flammulina brings true pleasure when cooked.

Mushrooms are prepared with various sauces, marinated, wrapped in bacon, and added to soups. Dry mushroom powder enhances and enriches the taste of any dish and sauce, corresponding to the climate requirements for its cultivation.

Growing it in summer, especially in hot regions, is not economically feasible since its preferred temperature is +12-14°C (54-57°F). And that's the maximum. We get better quality mushrooms at +8-10°C (46-50°F).

But in winter, growing it at +8-12°C (46-53°F), we save significantly on energy costs.

In general, technology with plastic collars is used in large enterprises where Enoki is grown in monoculture. They also use techniques for inducing fruiting, such as milling the surface of the block to remove stroma and lowering the temperature to +5°C (41°F) for 1-2 days.

In our farm conditions, reducing the temperature to such limits was impossible. That was solely to create synchronicity of fruiting, which is very important in a large enterprise in a monoculture. Due to the peculiarities of supplying our mushroom to the market, we were satisfied with the moderate prolongation of fruiting.

Therefore, we grew Flammulina at a temperature of +8-12°C (46-53°F) and a humidity of about 90%. Enoki is so tolerant of carbon dioxide that it was possible to maintain it at a level of 2000-3000 ppm due to complete 100% air recirculation. As a result, winter cultivation of Flammulina is very economically profitable.

So, on our farm, we did not use blast cooling. But, for initiation, they lightly massaged the surface of the block without opening it or destroying the surface of the substrate block. They just seemed to knock down the surface stroma – aerial mycelium – with a circular movement of the fingers and palm. Then, the block was left on the shelves for 3-5 days without opening. After the surface of the block was again covered with dense mycelium, the upper part of the bag was cut to leave the collar from this bag at its entire height. Thus, we imitated putting on a plastic collar as in large enterprises.

This collar is necessary to create a high level of CO_2 in the fruiting zone, which will stimulate the growth of the mushroom stem. Thanks to this, the legs will stretch up to 15-20 cm, and the caps will be the size of a pea.

These are Asian standards for this culture. It's not for nothing that they are also called Enoki, noodle mushrooms.

After the block was opened, another 5-7 days passed until primordia appeared on its surface. In yellow Flammulina, they looked like fish eggs – bright brown beads. The white one had cream-colored beads.

For another 3-5 days, they were passed from primordia to harvest, depending on the temperature in the chamber.

Flammulina mushroom picking is probably the easiest. You can hold the entire mushroom clump with a slight hand movement.

We did not notice any problems, infections, or diseases when growing Flamulina. The culture is very resistant to fluctuations in climate parameters. It tolerates direct moisture on fruiting bodies, and the temperature drops to +4-6°C (40-43°F). The maximum temperature at which Flammulina could grow is +15°C (60°F). But it is impossible to grow it for the market at this temperature. Mushrooms quickly open, release spores, and lose their elasticity. For home use and preparations for pickling and canning, this is an entirely suitable temperature. It is convenient to do at the end of the sales season.

It is necessary to pick mushrooms when the cap has not opened and is the size of a pea to sell them on the market.

For home use, we collected it when the cap was completely open. We believed that at this age, the harmonious taste was fully revealed.

After all, this is, by nature, a Winter honey fungus.

In this way, we grew this culture's white strain. The white strain, in combination with a long stem and a small cap, meets Asian standards, and we focus on them in our production.

Strain 2619, from the Ukrainian Kholodny Institute of Botany, has proven itself well. We became good friends with him and had no intention of changing him for another. It gave an excellent harvest of 20-22% in the first wave. The fruit bodies were snow-white, and the taste was fantastic.

I'll note right away that you need to focus on only one wave of fruiting because there is practically not second one, or it is not economically profitable.

Our primary customers were Asian restaurants in big cities in Ukraine. It was one of the most consumed mushrooms there. Restaurants could only get it from China and Korea, and because of this, its price was very high in the networks.

Plus, the mushroom was supplied in packages in a gas environment because the delivery times were significant. Accordingly, the taste was not distinguished by sophistication. Restaurants bought our fresh mushrooms with great pleasure, and sales only increased what we could not say about the Ukrainian consumer, who could not experience the culinary delights of this magnifiend mushroom.

Unfortunately, a war began at the very peak of sales, and we could never fully accelerate sales, although the conditions for this were all right.

So, with this technology and strain 2619, we covered the needs of Asian restaurant chefs but not the domestic market, which stubbornly was in no hurry to consume this beauty.

Then we found another way.

Beginning of fruiting

Mushrooms ready to pick

The yield is very high and often reaches 30-35%

We began to try to grow a **yellow Flammulina crop**, the so-called *Enoki aureus*, made of a typical wild forest crop.

We tested several strains from the same Kholodny Institute of Botany collection to do this. After much experimentation, strain 2337 took root with us. Slightly creamy, with gorgeous shapes of fruiting bodies.

For our domestic market, we have developed a completely different growing technology.

The block was not opened, but a side incision was made. A beautiful growth grew from the cut – a bouquet of mushrooms reminiscent of a Winter honey fungus growing on a stump.

The photo shows all the options and cultivation methods that were described above. You can also evaluate what mushrooms look like in packages grown differently.

This forest method gradually began to attract our internal customers, but the market needed to continue to develop in this direction.

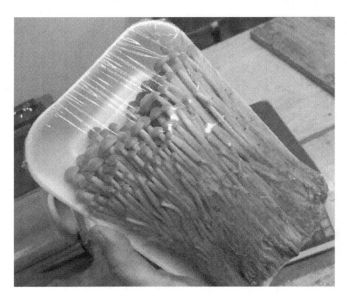

In general, we successfully grew Enoki, and the restaurant market was expanding constantly. There were Chinese and Vietnamese communities in almost all cities of Ukraine. The so-called "Chinese restaurants," with their characteristic Chinese cuisine, developed and became popular. In Asian cuisine, mushrooms, especially Enoki and Shimeji, are among the leaders in their cooking.

We ate Flammulina with great pleasure. We still liked the yellow one better. It had an aroma almost indistinguishable from that of the forest. In general, when you go into the chamber where Flammulina is grown, there is such a smell that you immediately understand what kind of mushroom is growing here. Flammulina exudes such a delicate fruity-caramel aroma that it feels like you are in a fairy forest. I even heard light notes of apricot in this aroma — an incredible feeling. I've always been fascinated by Flammulina. I could linger in the chamber for a while to look at hundreds of openwork mushrooms huddled close to each other with gracefully curved legs. I hope you share these feelings with me.

I can't help but feel that the European market does not yet deeply understand how tasty and healthy this product is. Therefore, Enoki has yet to expand the mushroom market in Europe and America.

Anyone can glean data from the Internet about the enormous quantities of Enoki consumed by the Asian market.

It is hundreds of thousands of tons per day. And whoever tries Enoki dishes at least once will love this mushroom forever.

Flammulina is great in soups and stir-fries with bacon and chicken.

It tastes delicious when marinated as an independent dish and even more so when mixed with other mushrooms. Especially in pickled form, it harmonizes with Oyster mushrooms or Pulmonaris.

But we successfully marinated it with Eringi, Shiitake, and Agrocybe. It may also be eaten fresh in salads. That is genuinely an excellent mushroom with a crunchy texture. When someone eats a dish from Enoki, a delicious crunch is heard around them. And it's very seductive and funny. We loved the Enoki dish, wrapped in bacon strips and stewed after frying in sweet and sour sauce.

For connoisseurs of forest mushrooms, the Winter honey fungus mushroom is suitable because it can subsequently grow on waste blocks right on the street and even in winter, under the snow, just as it happens in the forest. I captured such mushrooms on a used substrate on our farm. They were the same as in the winter forest. With the same velvety leg, bright coloring, and mucus on the surface. Taste and aroma were the same as that of the wild mushroom.

We also dried Enoki. Then, we grounded the dried mushrooms into powder and stored them in tightly closed spice containers. The powder had a peculiar caramel aroma and was excellent seasoning, especially for soups and broths.

CHAPTER 33

Agrocybe / Poplar Mushroom (Cyclocybe Aegerita (V. Brig.) Vizzini) Flammulina Velutipes, Pioppino, Velvet Shank, Tea Tree Mushroom, Yanagi-Matsutake

It is another representative of the Honey mushroom family. In Italy, it is more romantically called Pioppino.

In ancient Rome, poplar honey fungus was valued for its excellent taste. Its aroma is most like wild mushrooms. In Italy, it is affectionately called Pioppino and continues to conquer stomachs.

The nutritional value of these mushrooms lies in the high content of proteins, carbohydrates, and lipids, a unique substance of terpene nature: bristol A, phenolic substances with antioxidant properties, and selenium.

It has been scientifically proven that the use of Poplar honey fungus has a preventive effect in the fight against age-related changes, the development of malignant tumors, diabetes mellitus, and inflammatory diseases in the joints.

Growing technology

Sunflower husks, crushed cereal straw, and fine fractions of softwood are used to prepare the substrate. The substrate in the blocks must be well compacted and the surface smooth.

It guarantees that the fruiting bodies will grow only at the place of initiation and will not become deformed. Poplar honey fungus also loves dark bags for the substrate. That increases the growth rate by 2-3 times.

Bran, soybean, and corn flour are used as nutritional supplements. If you use wood as a base, this will lengthen the incubation period.

Optimal substrate indicators: humidity 63-65%; pH 6.5-7; total nitrogen content 1.3-1.5%; C/N ratio: 30-50/1.

Mycelium application rate is 2-5%

Incubation: 26-35 days; temperature +22-26°C (72-79°F); relative humidity 85-90%

Initiation: 7-10 days; temperature +13-15°C (57-60°F); humidity 95-99%; CO_2 0.1-1.5%; lighting 500-1000 lux.

There are 3 ways to open bags.

1. The bag is softly massaged on the substrate's surface and left closed. After primordia 1cm (0.3 inch) high appears, the package is cut off 5-10cm (2-4 inches) from the substrate.

2. Immediately cut off the package at a height of 5-10cm (2-4 inches) from the surface of the substrate. In this situation, a tranquil climate is needed during primordia formation; a strong airflow can dry out the surface, and primordia will not form.

3. Method 3 is used on dark bags. Release the air from the free part of the bag, fix it, place the block on a shelf on its side or upside down, and make cuts in the bag. Fruiting bodies will then form only at the cut site.

Fruiting: 4-6 days; temperature +13-17°C (57-64°F): humidity 90-95% CO_2 0.1-0.12%

When cultivating Agrocybe, you must remember that this crop is inferior to other cultivated mushrooms in terms of productivity. The maximum we could grow was 16-18% over three waves of fruiting.

It is no longer profitable to initiate more waves, and besides, the Agrocybe substrate is very fond of the mushroom midge, which settles in it even during the first wave, not to mention subsequent ones. On the third wave, there is already quite a lot of fliyi around in the chamber. In general, they do not cause any harm to the mushrooms themselves. And on the third wave, the mushrooms are not wormy and pretty marketable. But the very fact of the presence of midges in the chamber takes place.

By the way, when compact lamps for killing mosquitoes appeared on the Chinese market with a standard H22 base, we successfully began using them in a chamber with Agrocybe.

Its effectiveness was relatively high. I poured a cup of dead midges out of it twice a day.

Although a grown midge can be destroyed, the eggs it has already laid in the substrate and larvae continue the life cycle, and destroying them is impossible.

Therefore, many mushroom growers mistakenly try to fight the midge itself, not realizing that they must combat the source of its occurrence. Since the source of eggs and pupae cannot be defeated, dealing with rotten substrate, mushrooms, and waste from mushroom growing is necessary.

A comment:

Like other insects, Drosophila, or fruit fly (Drosophila melanogaster), goes through several stages of its development. These stages include:

1. Egg: The fruit fly's life cycle begins with the laying of eggs. Eggs are usually laid on food, the surface of fruits, or rotting vegetables and mushrooms.

2. Larva: Larvae are born from eggs. They actively feed and develop, passing through several larval stages. They usually feed on rotting fruits and vegetables, mushrooms, and substrate.

3. Pupa: The fruit fly develops into a pupa after the last larval stage. The pupa is a stationary stage in which critical processes of metamorphosis occur.

4. Imago (adult): After metamorphosis, the pupa splits open, and an adult called the imago emerges. It is a fully formed insect with wings, eyes, antennae, and other characteristic features. Drosophila adults are ready to reproduce and begin to look for a partner to mate with and lay eggs, thus completing the fly`s life cycle.

Thus, Drosophila`s life cycle includes four main stages: egg, larva, pupa, and adult (imago). Each of these stages plays a role in the insect`s development.

5. Entry: In this context, the life cycle of Drosophila begins with the pest`s entry into a mushroom-growing facility. Adults may enter the premises through windows, doors, or other openings.

6. Reproduction: Adult individuals begin reproduction after the pest enters the enterprise. They lay eggs on the surface of mushroom fruiting tissue or the substrate used to grow mushrooms.

7. Development of larvae: Drosophila larvae hatch from the eggs and actively feed on the fungal substrate, damaging its structure and decreasing yield.

8. Damage and losses: Drosophila larvae continue to develop, causing significant damage to the fungal substrate. It can lead to a decrease in the quality and quantity of the harvest and financial losses for the enterprise.

Thus, Drosophila, acting as a pest in mushroom-growing enterprises, can cause serious problems, reducing the yield and damaging the mushroom substrate.

Let's continue. The incubation mode is standard for most crops.

When the block is already ripe, it has a dense structure, a creamy tint, and light brown pigment spots of thick exudate that are visible under the film. In this state, the block is ready for fruiting. If necessary, the substrate can be kept in the incubator for up to 30 days, but no more. After this, fruiting bodies develop under the film and are already in the incubator.

If the block is made using our standard bags with a filter, then there have been cases when we grew high-quality mushrooms without even opening the bag. That is, the mushrooms grew right under the film. At this time, the CO_2 level inside the block probably exceeded even 5000 ppm. That indicates Agrocybe's high tolerance for carbon dioxide. Again, this property can be successfully used to save energy resources. That is, to organize a climate without supplying fresh air, with further costs for heating or cooling it.

Agrocybe grows well in a wide temperature range, from 57 to 80F. However, it is more of a heat-loving crop. Humidity is 85-90%. Based on this, Agrocybe will be an excellent neighbor to Shiitake and have the exact climate requirements.

But there are several features.

When the block is opened, leave a 5-7cm (2-3 inches) collar and reduce air movement as much as possible. Any excessive air movement during the primordia formation, even with high humidity, will dry out the surface of the substrate, and then we may not see mushrooms at all. Or only single kinds.

In such cases, the chamber with Agrocybe should be quiet, stuffy, and humid at this time. This is precisely what it needs at this stage of development.

Alternatively, waiting for the primordia without opening the top of the package can prevent such drying out. They can form well right under the film.

Then, it can be opened when fruiting bodies are 1-3cm (0.3-1) inch high. There is no need to worry that something will happen to them in the film; this is just a comfortable environment for them.

We see this situation in the photo below.

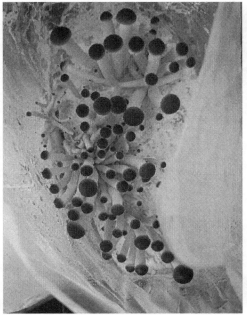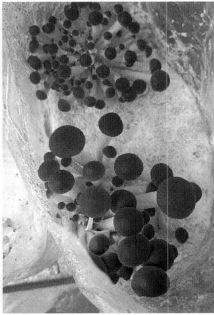

However, care must ensure the mushroom opens partially. It is necessary to pick as soon as the cap`s edges have come off or are just about to come off the stem. Then, sporulation has not yet begun, and we will get a juicy, thick stem and the same cap. If we miss this moment, we will end up with a thin, stiff leg and a hat with brittle edges, which will be light and unattractive.

If the mushroom is picked on time, its cap will be an attractive dark brown color, and it will be one of those cultivated mushrooms with a forest mushroom aroma.

A mushroom with a fast growth rate must be collected twice daily, even if the temperature is 60F. If it is higher, then three times.

We once received a large order to supply this mushroom to Kharkiv. We didn't have enough substrate for such a large order, so we had to buy more from a colleague from Zaporizhzhia. We then wholly loaded one chamber only with Agrocybe blocks.

It was then that I had to collect three times a day.

But the mushrooms were always in suitable condition.

Then, our load was complete. In addition to the two chambers where Shiitake, Hericium, and Flammluina were supposed to bear fruit, we also had to collect 44 pounds of Agrocybe daily. They also had to be packaged and mailed to the recipient on the same day.

We finished work on the farm late in the evening. But the order was completed.

The photo shows how these blocks bore fruit back then.

Tip: pack these mushrooms with substrate particles that remain on the stems after harvesting. In this case, the mushrooms are stored well.

We have significantly increased sales volumes of this mushroom in local markets and sent it packaged to large cities in Ukraine. The Kharkiv market increased its monthly consumption, and we could no longer keep up with them. A good distributor worked there and, in a short period, introduced this mushroom to most stores. Sales grew expo nentially. He also increased sales of shiitake. We have already begun to think about expanding the enterprise.

Unfortunately, the first days of the war took place in Kharkiv. Our dealer was never able to receive our last ample supply of mushrooms. We just heard from him on the phone that his warehouses with goods and our mushrooms were bombed and on fire.

We then completely loaded one chamber only with Agrocybe blocks

CHAPTER 34

Shimeji White (Beech Mushroom) Hypsizygus Marmoreus; White Marbled Mushroom; Marble Honey Fungus; Bunapi-Shimeji

Shimeji is one of the most popular gourmet mushrooms in Southeast Asia.

The cultivation of Honey mushrooms is widespread in Japan and China, where two types of Honey mushrooms have been successfully cultivated: white and brown Beech mushrooms.

The name Marble honey fungus comes from the very light color of the fruiting body, on which stains like marble form when moisture is present.

Shimeji is rich in fiber, protein, and vitamin E, which positively affects metabolism and helps improve body tone. Fruiting bodies contain selenium, an antioxidant that protects cells from damage and prevents the creation of tumors. Regular consumption of the mushroom prevents obesity, diabetes, and allergic reactions and improves the functioning of the immune system.

White mushrooms are valued in oriental cuisine due to their rich, sweetish-nutty taste and crispy structure.

The mushroom goes well with meat and seafood and is used in sauces and soups. Its flavor develops best when fried with a small amount of butter.

Growing technology

The substrate consists of sunflower husks and chopped straw, with softwood making up no more than 20% of the base's total mass. The nutrient additives bran, soy, and corn flour comprise 25-30% of the substrate's total mass.

Humidity 63-68%; pH 6.5; total nitrogen content 1.5-1.9% C/N ratio: 25-30/1; density 500-700kg/m3 (31-44lb/ft^3).

The application rate of planting grain mycelium is 3-5% of the total mass of the substrate.

Incubation: 40-50d; temperature +21-23°C (72-77°F); humidity 85-90%

Formation of primordia: 5-8 days; temperature +10-15°C (50-59°F); humidity 95-99%; CO_2 0.05-0.1% lighting 500-1000 lux.

Fruiting: 5-10 days; temperature +13-17C (57-64F); humidity 85-95%; CO_2 0.1-0.15%.

It`s a fascinating mushroom. Productivity is high and stable, up to 25%.

The mushroom is fleshy, snow-white, and tasty. It is precisely this bright white color that scares off the European buyer. It has an association with the Toadstool. But the same restaurants that bought Enoki from us also happily bought Shimeji.

And in general, when we offered it to them, they were delighted to have this mushroom in their assortment.

Shimeji's harvest is even easier than Enoki's. The entire bunch is separated from the substrate with a slight movement of one hand.

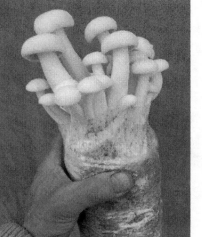

Fresh mushrooms are like rubber, dense and springy. It is not damaged during packaging and transportation and can be stored well for up to 14 days.

We grew it in the same chamber with Agrocybe. It is generally very tolerant of climate parameters, so it will grow well with different crops in different climates – an easy mushroom to grow. The main thing is to find a market for it. The photo shows how charming and attractive it is.

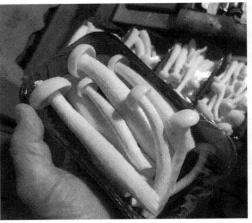

CHAPTER 35

Shimeji Gray (Buna Shimeji)

This species differs from the White Shimeji in that its cap is gray and has a structural mesh on its surface, similar to a turtle shell.

But it does not have such a long and fleshy leg. Buna shimeji is best grown in compact clumps.

In our conditions, incubation period was 35-40 days. The growing period coincided with warm weather; therefore, initiation was required to lower the temperature after incubation to +12°C (54°F). Otherwise, the block did not want to wake up and begin bearing fruit.

CHAPTER 36

Eryngii (Pleurotus Eryngii (DC.) Quél) Steppe Oyster Mushroom, King Oyster Mushroom, White Steppe Mushroom

King oyster mushroom is the most common and best-selling mushroom on the internet. Its sales levels were constantly growing here, too. We sold it quite often in local markets and the capital.

Steppe oyster mushrooms have gained popularity due to their shape and culinary qualities. They have dense, white stem flesh with a delicate, sweetish taste. King oyster mushrooms have great nutritional value combined with their unique taste.

Fruiting bodies are rich in protein and amino acids: aspartic, glutamic, and arginine. Contains vitamins C, B2, B1, B5, A, D, minerals K. Mg. Na. Ca

Also, the fruiting bodies of King oyster mushrooms contain many biologically active substances that benefit the body, help prevent atherosclerosis, and positively affect the functioning of the liver and kidneys. Polysaccharide Pleurin effectively lowers blood pressure, cholesterol, and blood sugar levels and has immunomodulatory, antibacterial, antiviral, and antifungal effects.

Growing technology

The raw materials for King oyster mushroom's substrate are crushed cereal straw, sunflower husks, corn waste, and alder sawdust. The content of protein compounds is crucial for the King oyster mushroom substrate. Cereal bran, corn flour, flax and rapeseed, sunflower, and soybean meal are nutritional herbal additives.

The optimal substrate parameters for growing King oyster mushrooms are humidity 65-70%, pH 6.5, total nitrogen content 01.5-1.9%, C/N ratio 25-30/1, and density 450-600 kg/m3 (28-38lb/ft^3).

The recommended rate for introducing planting mycelium is 3-5% by substrate weight and mix thoroughly to speed up and improve the incubation quality.

We used the following substrate composition:

Straw pellets – 30%

Sunflower husk pellets – 30%

Corn flour – 10%

Wheat bran – 20%

Soy flour or meal – 10%

Gypsum – 1%

Microclimate parameters during incubation:

Incubation lasts 20-30 days; temperature +21-23°C (71-75°F); humidity 85-95%; CO2 0.5-2.0%

Formation of primordia: 7-10 days; temperature +10-15°C (50-59°F); humidity 95-99%; CO2 0.05-0.1%; lighting 500-1000 lux.

To initiate the release of primordia, we used two methods.

1 – on the substrate`s surface, gently massage through the bag and make a small cut at the top of the bag. Wait for the caps to form on the primordia and cut the package at the level of the substrate.

2 – on the substrate`s surface, do a hard massage with damage to the upper part, release the air, fix the edge of the bag, and place the block on the shelf upside down. Make a cross-shaped cut across the entire area of the bottom of the block and slightly raise the edges of the bag. After 5-7 days, primordia will begin to form, and as the mushrooms grow, the edges of the cut will diverge, and mushrooms will occupy the entire surface. With this method, monitoring climate parameters and preventing temperature changes is vital.

Fruiting: 5-8 days; temperature +11-17°C (52-64°F); humidity 85-95%; CO_2 0.1-0.15%.

The number and shape of King oyster mushroom mushrooms can be adjusted during growth: if you need large mushrooms, as soon as primordia have formed and leaders have emerged, 2-4 of the most beautiful ones are left on the block, and all the rest are removed at the substrate level with a knife. This procedure is unnecessary If you need medium and small fruiting bodies.

If you need large fruiting bodies with a large stem and a small cap, increase the CO_2 level to 0.15%. If you need a mushroom with a large cap and a short stem, increase the supply of fresh air and keep the CO_2 level within 0.08-0.1%.

The overall productivity of King oyster mushrooms ranges from 250 und 500g aus 1 kg (0.5 to 1.1 pound from 2.2 pounds) of substrate per wave of fruiting. Still, it directly depends on the characteristics of the substrate and maintaining the required climate.

Biological activity reaches 130-180%. With such indicators, the second wave is unproductive, and growing it is better.

Steppe oyster mushroom has a long shelf life. At 0-2°C degrees, mushrooms do not lose their properties and elasticity for up to 20-25 days. A highly effective storage method is vacuum packaging with air pumping out, allowing you to store mushrooms for up to 30 days.

Therefore, we found a convenient way: we put mushrooms, about 3kg

(6.6 pounds), in a plastic bag and then created a vacuum with an ordinary vacuum cleaner. The mushrooms were tightly covered with film and could be stored and safely transported.

Of course, King oyster mushrooms are quite inconsistent in cultivation. Changes in climate parameters are not suitable for them. Therefore, we will discuss them in more detail here.

The fungus does not like the presence of condensation or free moisture on the fruiting bodies. In such cases, its growth stops, the fruiting bodies quickly die, and bacteriosis immediately begins to appear on them. Bacteriosis on King oyster mushrooms is expected if you do not monitor it carefully. It may even become widespread. In such cases, stopping the growing process and disinfecting the chamber was necessary. It also worked well, transferring the cultivation to another chamber.

Also, unlike other mushrooms, shiitakes require a reasonably stable temperature in the growing chamber. That is important so that the chamber temperature does not exceed the dew point when the chamber temperature changes. If this situation is harmless for Shiitakes, it can be disastrous for King oyster mushrooms.

In this book`s format, we will not be able to reveal the theory of this problem deeply enough. We must introduce the reader to the Mollier diagram and teach how to apply it in practice. We will cover this topic in subsequent books aimed at advanced mushroom growers working as technologists at large enterprises.

We often hold seminars and presentations for such specialists.

Here, we will emphasize to the reader that the growth of King oyster mushrooms must be constantly monitored to notice the problem in time. For example, if the leg has become rough and slightly cracked, there is a discrepancy between the growth of internal and superficial tissues. The mushroom grower often perceives this as the mushroom drying out and subconsciously begins to increase the humidity. And the situation is only getting worse. But the real reason was that the fungus started to breathe worse. By respiration, we mean the ability of the fungus to evaporate moisture. Therefore, the CO_2 level is irrelevant, and King oyster mushrooms grow calmly even at 1500 ppm. However, the presence of a dew point can partially or even completely stop the evaporation of water from the mushroom's surface and, therefore, cease its respiration. Long-term exposure to such negative parameters can lead to defects in fruiting bodies and even death.

King oyster mushrooms also do not like directional solid air currents. They need to be organized so that the direction is either up or to the sides, but not towards the mushrooms.

The Chinese Eagle strain has taken root well on our farm. The Dutch strain from Micelia, M2603, is also terrific.

And so, you brought the blocks from the incubator into the growing chamber.

First, initiation is recommended by sharply lowering the temperature to +8°C (46°F). However, this is typical for large cultivation volumes in enterprises where King oyster mushrooms are grown in monoculture.

This technique is necessary to synchronize fruiting. We don't need this on our home farm. On the contrary, a certain prolongation in fruiting only makes it more convenient for us.

Therefore, we place the blocks from the incubator into a chamber with a temperature of +14-16°C (57-60°F) and a humidity of 85-97%.

Currently, as a rule, there are already fruitful blocks in the chamber. Therefore, the climate will have to be managed so that it is suitable for each.

In general, to stimulate the release of primordia at the initial stage, it is desirable to maintain the highest possible humidity — 95-98% and reduce air flows as much as possible. CO_2 at this time can be up to 2000-3000 ppm.

To stimulate primordia formation, you can perform a light massage of the upper surface of the substrate.

Without opening the package, we destroy the upper fluffy part of the mycelium with some effort by running our fingers through the film. The blocks are then left standing on the shelves in the chamber.

Primordia will appear on the surface on the 7th to 10th day after this. The package can be opened when the primordia is 2-3cm (0.7-1 inches) high. If we open it at 5cm (1.1-2 inches) height, we will get more large mushrooms but fewer. Only the leaders will survive in the film, and the weak will die.

In the first case, there will be more mushrooms, but they will be medium-sized. The film must be cut to the top edge of the block.

Many fruits can be formed.

If nothing is done, they will all grow small, and there will be a shortage of harvest.

In this case, separating or thinning part of the fruiting bodies is necessary. For our blocks, leaving 5-8 mushrooms for fruiting was optimal.

Separation is done by cutting out excess and weak mushrooms with a knife or breaking them out.

We have developed our version of opening blocks, which differs from the classic one. We are delighted with it and have successfully used it.

It works like this.

After the blocks are placed on the shelves in the chamber, we immediately open them, hand-clean everything on the surface – stroma, mycelium, and rudiments – and roll the film into an envelope.

Then we turn the block over and place it on the shelf with the bottom up.

Then, we make a cross-shaped cut on the bottom. After 5-7 days, the primordia begins to emerge from the incision. We also control and regulate their quantity. After another week, the mushrooms are ready to be harvested.

You can also cut not on the heel but on the side surface. Everyone should try all these options on their farm to choose the best one.

We liked this system for its simplicity and ease of use. The mushrooms were usually of excellent quality. Plus, harvesting with this technology is 5-6 days earlier.

The photo report shows the entire sequence of actions and the final result.

If, for some reason, the block gave away less than 20% of the harvest in the first wave, we can leave it for the second wave. If we receive 20-25% in the first wave, then immediately after collection, the blocks go for disposal.

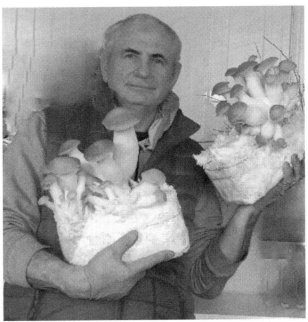

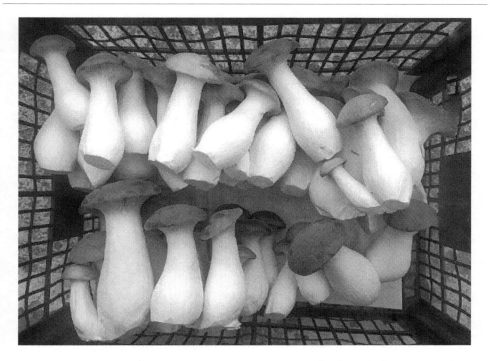

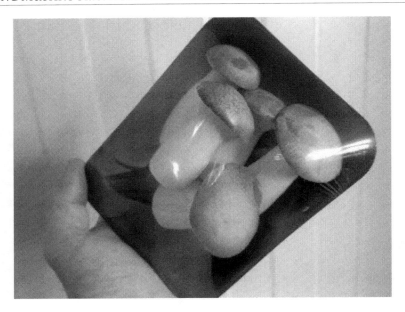

We no longer had time to pack it into containers for shipping. Therefore, we found a convenient way: we put about 6.6 pounds of mushrooms in a plastic bag and then used an ordinary vacuum cleaner to create a vacuum. The mushrooms were tightly covered with film, and the briquettes could be placed in a box. Since the mushrooms were immobilized and pressed tightly against each other, they were well transported without damage.

CHAPTER 37

Oyster Mushroom (Pleurotus Ostreatus (Fr.) Quél.)

It is one of the very common cultivated mushrooms.

In Ukraine, this crop occupies a large part of the mushroom market. Oyster mushroom shares the market in this segment of inexpensive champignon mushrooms. We consider Oyster mushrooms to be more culinaryly delicious than champignons. It only loses in the form of fruiting bodies.

The fruiting bodies of Oyster mushrooms are rich in a large amount of bioactive endopolysaccharides. It has been proven that they contain the entire spectrum of essential amino acids, zinc, phosphorus, B vitamins, and sulfur, in quantities that satisfy the body's daily need for these elements.

It has been scientifically proven that oyster mushroom fruiting bodies can be medicinally valuable for a wide range of diseases. The polysaccharide B-glucan has a strong anti-inflammatory effect and may effectively treat hay fever. Regular consumption of Oyster mushrooms has a preventive effect on the body during the progression of diabetes mellitus and lowers blood sugar levels. It benefits the digestive system and is a preventative against digestive tract cancer.

Growing technology

The basis for the substrate composition can be grain straw, sunflower husks, flax, and cotton husks – vegetable additives: bran and corn or soy flour.

Optimal substrate indicators: humidity 65-70%; pH 7.5; total nitrogen content 0.7%; C/N ratio 70/1; density 400-450 kg/m3. (25-28lb/ft^3).

The optimal application rate of planting mycelium is 2-3% by substrate weight. Due to the high activity of mycelium development, mixing the mycelium with the substrate is recommended to avoid overheating thoroughly.

Incubation: Incubation of Oyster mushroom blocks is very fast, 10-14 days; temperature +23-27°C (75-82°F); air humidity 70-75%; CO2 0.2-0.3%.

Cuts are made on the film to initiate fruiting.

Remove the air from the bag to fix the free edge. That stimulates the growth of primordia into the incision. Primordia will appear after 3-5 days. Temperature +13-15°C (57-60°F); humidity 85-95%; CO2 1.0-1.2%; lighting 200-300 lux.

Fruiting: Temperature +15-20°C (60-70°F); relative humidity 90-95%; CO2 0.07-0.09% lighting 200-300 lux.

The overall productivity of Oyster mushrooms is 180-350g pro 1 kg (6.3-12.3 ounces per 2.2) pounds of substrate for 2 waves of fruiting, depending on the quality of the substrate and microclimatic conditions. Biological efficiency reaches 100%.

Mushroom picking is the easiest. You twist the druses and place them in one layer of a container.

After harvesting, you need to quickly cool the mushrooms to a temperature from 0°C to +1°C (32 to 34°F) and store them packed in film since mushrooms lose much moisture when unpacked. Keep in the refrigerator for more than two weeks.

When grown, oyster mushrooms are quite inconsistent concerning climate parameters.

It is sensitive to temperature and humidity changes, weather transitions from winter to spring, and air currents.

We grew strain K17 with undoubtedly beautiful and marketable fruiting bodies. It had one crucial advantage – this was the only strain that could be grown at CO2 levels up to 1100 ppm and sometimes even 1200 ppm. Most Oyster mushroom strains prefer a carbon dioxide level of no more than 700-900 ppm. And this, with the correct climate organization, made growing K17 at a lower cost possible. I'll say right away that growing

Oyster mushrooms at 700 ppm and 1100 ppm is a big difference in energy costs for heating the chamber, which can be very significant.

In our case, the substrate composition consisted of briquettes of sunflower husk 40%, straw 40%, and wheat bran 20% in dry matter. Gypsum is 1% as a mineral additive, and substrate humidity is 65%.

Let's focus on climate.

Its optimal parameters lie in the range of temperature +13-17°C (57-64°F) and humidity 85-90%. The level of carbon dioxide in the chamber is, on average, 850-1000+ppm.

Let's look at the details.

As soon as the blocks with Oyster mushrooms are placed from the incubator into the fruiting chamber, the temperature must be set to +13-17°C (57-64°F), humidity 90-95%, and CO2 level 1000-1200ppm.

These are precisely the parameters under which initiation to fruiting will occur well.

If an incision is used as perforation, we carefully observe the moment the mycelial cord appears. It is a tubercle of mycelium that will border the cut. These are the first signs of the appearance of primordia. At this time, it is necessary to maintain humidity at least 90% and reduce airflow as much as possible so as not to dry out the perforations and initiate the exit of the primordia. We continue to keep the CO2 level relatively high – 1200 ppm.

When primordia emerge en masse from the perforations, the humidity must be lowered to 85% and the airflow increased by half. At this age, primordia are very susceptible to changes in temperature and humidity, especially strain K17. Therefore, we keep the parameters as stable as possible. Lower the temperature to +17-20°C (57-60°F).

In general, if anyone is familiar with the Mollier diagram, the parameters, temperature +20C 60F, and humidity 85%, are just within the required limits and are far from the "dew point," which is generally destructive for mushrooms, and even more so for Oyster mushrooms. The K17 strain is even more susceptible to it.

Therefore, if your climate control system cannot maintain a temperature close to +20C (60F) in winter, good Oyster mushrooms can be grown at lower temperatures, +11-13°C (53-57°F), and even lower. The main thing is, when the temperature drops, make sure not to fall to the dew point. For this, as a rule, it is necessary to synchronously reduce humidity with a decrease in temperature. At +11°C (53°F), the humidity should be above 80%, and at +10°C (50°F), not above 75%. Air flows at this time must be reduced to not dry out the mushrooms.

Therefore, even at such critical temperatures, it is possible to grow good Oyster mushrooms. According to the algorithm described above, you must carefully monitor climate parameters and respond quickly to changes.

These are general principles for creating a climate in Oyster mushroom growing chambers. When, at the very beginning, we grew only oyster mushrooms in all chambers, we developed complete regulations on climate parameters and strictly adhered to them to avoid defects that could destroy up to 50% of the crop.

I have touched upon only a tiny fraction of such regulations' details and features here. However, in the concept of this book, there is no need to consider all this in full because, on a home farm, we will have different conditions associated with growing different mushroom cultures in one chamber. Therefore, choosing a compromise climate for all crops will be necessary.

On our farm, we generally organized an average compromise climate for three crops and placed them in one chamber. These are King oyster mushrooms, Shiitake mushrooms, and Oyster mushrooms. We obtained high-quality mushrooms from all three crops by choosing the parameters mode, temperature +13°C (57°F), humidity 85-90%, and CO_2 level up to 1200 ppm.

The photo shows the Oyster mushroom we got. The K17 strain is top-notch – beautiful, dark, and juicy.

No matter the strict climate requirements, growing good mushrooms of different crops in one chamber is possible if you wish and pay due attention.

You can see the dynamics of mushroom growth in the photo.

Mushrooms are at the stage of technical maturity and can be harvested.

Option for fruiting on top of the block

CHAPTER 38

Lung Oyster Mushroom or Pulmonarius

Let us separately dwell on one of the Oyster mushroom varieties – Pulmonaris (Lung oyster mushroom).

This species stands out from the varieties of Oyster mushrooms.

It has differences in the shape of the fruiting bodies, growing conditions, and taste.

The Lung oyster mushroom has a slightly sweet taste, the flesh is crispy, and the stem, although elongated, is edible. Some buyers prefer this type of Oyster mushroom.

So, Lung oyster mushroom is very tolerant to climate conditions and grows well under various temperatures and humidity. It can be successfully grown in the temperature range from +11 to 23°C (53 to 75°F) and moisture 75-95%.

The dew point is not scary for her. At this point, the fungus's growth stops, but it cannot die.

In general, it is a beautiful variety for cultivation, but for some reason, unlike the Oyster mushroom, the buyer is not so actively buying it. Therefore, we grew it in smaller quantities. When pickled, the Lung oyster mushroom is simply magnificent and tastier than the Oyster mushroom.

It would help if you were also prepared for sporulation in this crop, which is higher than in other mushrooms. Pickers often have trouble with sporulation, so high-quality protective equipment is necessary.

The productivity of Lung oyster mushroom on non-sterile substrate technology is 25-27% on three waves of fruiting. And for sterile – 25-30%, on one or two waves. Often, one wave is enough to grow about 25% of the crop, and then blocks are needed for disposal.

In general, a very productive culture.

CHAPTER 39

Golden Oyster Mushroom (Pleurotus Citrinopileatus Singer), Lemon Oyster Mushroom, Limonka, Citrino, Yellow Oyster Mushroom, Ilmak, Tamogitake

It is a charming representative of the Pleurotus family.

You have to look at its photo and feel the charm of this mushroom culture – graceful shape, thin legs, soft yellow hat, exudes a fresh aroma. Well, why not a super lady in the world of mushrooms?

It is one of the few types of mushrooms that can be eaten even raw, for example, in vegetable salads.

If you fry, do it quickly, no more than 5 minutes, to preserve maximum initial aroma and texture.

Vitamins of group B were identified in the fruiting bodies of Oyster mushrooms: B3, B5, folic acid, vitamin A, and amino acids: valine, lysine, leucine, and glutamic acid.

Scientific experiments have confirmed the presence of natural substances with antiviral, antitumor, antibacterial, immunomodulatory, and anti-inflammatory effects in the Oyster mushroom fruiting bodies.

Regularly consuming Yellow oyster mushrooms significantly affects weight loss, cholesterol, and triglyceride levels and promotes natural body rejuvenation.

Growing technology

The substrate`s composition includes crushed cereal straw, sunflower husk, legume hay, bran, rapeseed, soybean meal, and corn flour.

We used the same composition for Oyster mushrooms.

Optimal substrate indicators: humidity 63-68%; pH 7-7.5; total nitrogen content 0.7-0.9%; C/N ratio 50-80/1; density 350-500kg/m3 (22-31lb/ft³).

The rate of application of grain mycelium is 2.5-4.5% by weight of the substrate.

Incubation: 10-14 days; temperature +23-26°C (75-80°F); relative humidity 85-95%; CO2 0.5-2.0%

Formation of primordia:

Temperature 60F; humidity 95-98%; CO2 0.5-0.8%; lighting 500-1000 lux.

Fruiting: 5-7 days per wave; relative humidity 90-95% CO2 0.5-1.0%.

The total productivity of Yellow oyster mushrooms is from 100g und 350g aus 1000g (3.5-12.3 ounces per 35.2 ounces) of substrate for 2 to 3 waves of fruiting.

The cap's edges are fragile, so mushrooms must be collected cautiously.

Store packaged in the refrigerator at +1 to +2°C (34 to 37°F) for up to 3 weeks.

Growing is no different from oyster mushrooms. It loves fresh air, so it is more comfortable with CO2 no above 700-800ppm. At a temperature in the chamber up to +15°C (60°F), a bright yellow color of the cap is obtained; with increasing temperature in the chamber, the color of the cap will be lighter.Yellow oyster mushrooms have a unique floral aroma and can be eaten raw in salads.It looks excellent packed in mixes.

 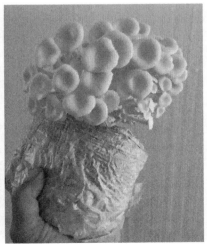

CHAPTER 40

Pink Oyster Mushroom (Pleurotus Djamor (Rumph. Ex Fr.) Boedijn, Pleurotus Salmoneostramineus Lj.N. Vassiljeva) Salmon Oyster Mushroom, Pink Flamingo

It is another representative of the elite from the **Pleurotus** family.

For me, it is associated with a woman in her prime.

There are gorgeous broad petals on mushroom caps, which resemble a rose together. As a man, I admire its curves. That's why I have a lot of photos and videos of this culture.

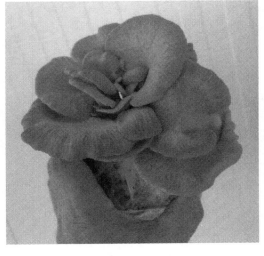

The fruiting bodies of Pink oyster mushrooms contain a high content of aspartic acid, which stimulates protein synthesis and lowers the ammonia level in the blood, normalizing liver function. An antiparasitic effect has been proven when consumed by these mushrooms; they also have a beneficial impact on lipid metabolism in people with excess body weight or with age-related problems. Even physiological damage to the liver, kidneys, and brain can be eliminated thanks to the beneficial effects of Oyster mushrooms on the body with regular use.

Growing technology

Substrates based on crushed grain straw, sunflower, buckwheat husks, flax kernels, sawdust, and plant nutritional supplements such as bran and corn flour are used to grow Pink oyster mushrooms.

We used the same substrate composition on our farm as for Oyster mushrooms.

Optimal substrate indicators: humidity 63-68%; pH 7.5; total nitrogen content 0.7-0.9%; C/N ratio 50-80/1; density 350-500 kg/m3. (22-31lb/ft^3).

The grain mycelium application rate is 2-3.5% of the total mass of the substrate. Thoroughly mixing of the substrate with mycelium accelerates the substrate`s colonization process.

Incubation: 14-25d; temperature +23-27°C (75-82°F); humidity 80-90%; CO2 content 0.3-0.5%.

Formation of primordia: 5-7d; temperature +15-17°C (60-64°F); humidity 95-99% CO2 0.05-0.1%; lighting intensity 750-1500 lux.

Fruiting: 5-8d; temperature +17-25°C (64-78°F); humidity 85-95%; CO2 0.1-0.15%.

The total productivity of Pink oyster mushrooms is 200-350g pro 1 kg (7-12.3 ounces per 2.2 pounds) of substrate for 3 waves of fruiting.

The biological efficiency of the substrate ranges from 50 to 120% depending on the microclimate conditions and its quality.

After picking, cool the mushrooms to +1°C (35°F), pack, and store at a temperature not lower than +6°C (43°F). The cold causes the fruiting bodies to turn brown and lose their quality. Shelf life is up to 10 days from the date of collection.

Growing this species is almost no different from growing the Oyster mushroom. However, like a spoiled woman, she loves warmth. That is, it must be grown at temperatures above +15C (60F). The best is +17-23°C (64-75°F). The closer the temperature is to +17C (64F), the brighter the color. At +22-23°C (73-75°F), it grows as well, but the pink tones will be paler.

When fried, it tastes like bacon. It`s a little harsh, but this will only give her a kind of meatiness. In its raw form, the taste of the mushroom is slightly sour – it pairs ideally in dishes with vegetables, meat, and fish.

It also looks excellent packaged in mixes.

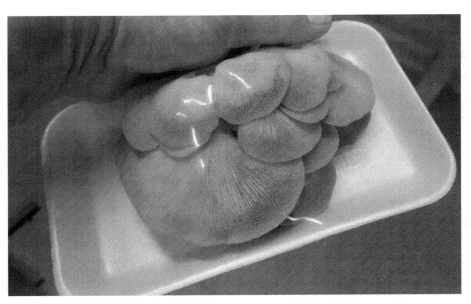

CHAPTER 41

Nameko Mushroom (Pholiota Nameko)

Another member of the cultivated mushroom family that I'm always delighted with!

That is Pholiota, but we attribute it to honey mushrooms. Well, look, isn't it a honey fungus?

1. **Nameko (Pholiota nameko)** is an edible mushroom widely used in cooking, especially in Japanese cuisine. Its sensitive flavor and unique texture make it a widespread ingredient in soups, stews, and other dishes.

2. **Useful and medicinal properties:** This mushroom contains vitamins, minerals, and nutrients, including vitamins D and B2, lots of fiber, and natural antibiotics that help fight staph infections and effectively eliminate inflammatory processes in the body.

In 1987, Ying claimed that an aqueous solution and a sodium hydroxide solution obtained from these mushrooms were 60% and 90% effective, respectively, against sarcoma 180 (this experiment was carried out on white mice in which tissue infected with sarcoma was implanted). Also, they significantly increase the body's resistance to staphylococcus bacteria. It is unknown whether Western scientists carried out any studies. The treatment results mentioned were obtained in China.

3. **Use in cooking:** Pholiota is often added to various dishes to add aroma, flavor, and texture. The mushroom has a delicate texture and a very unusual taste; for these qualities, it is highly valued in Asian cuisine. Salads, miso soup, stews, snacks, and broths are prepared from Japanese honey mushrooms. Nameko tastes excellent when fried, as its crunchy texture complements its sweet flavor. It is important to note that Japanese honey fungus retains most of its medicinal properties after heat treatment.

Nameko (Pholiota nameko) prefers to grow in temperate climates and is often found in wooded areas with temperate or humid climates. It usually grows in the subtropical and temperate zones in countries such as Japan, China, Korea, and some regions of Europe.

This fungus prefers to grow on trees or stumpy debris, especially on the woody mass of deciduous species such as oak, birch, and maple.

It can usually be found in places with a constant moisture supply, such as near bodies of water or in high-humidity conditions.

In nature, Nameko often grows in autumn and sometimes in spring. It can be found on fallen trees, especially previously damaged or diseased ones.

For a long time, we could not "disperse this culture." In the beginning, there was no excellent productive strain. The one that came to us was isolated from a wild crop and did not have the required yield. Judging by the publications of the same Chinese and Japanese fellow mushroom growers, it potentially has the most potent yield.

Nameko is also called "Japanese honey fungus" because, in Japan, it is consumed as much as the winter honey mushroom Enoki.

The first photo shows what we obtained from wild experimental mycelium, which came to us from the Kyiv Kholodny Institute of Botany collection.

Then, we stopped our experiments until we purchased mycelium from Mycelia, M4190.

Having worked out the substrate formula, in which we added more wood base and partly straw, we still came to excellent results. Our blocks began to produce up to 25-30% yield in one wave.

Considering its robust yield, it is a very cost-effective mushroom to grow.

It also has its drawbacks in cultivation.

First, we must create almost 100% humidity in the growing chamber. Sometimes, even at 95%, the surface of the substrate can dry out, causing the yield to decrease or even disappear entirely sharply.

Because of these moisture requirements, it is challenging to grow with other mushrooms.

Secondly, on the surface of its cap, there is a relatively thick layer of mucus, similar in consistency to boletus mucus. That makes it challenging to collect mushrooms. Also, substrate particles can fall on this mucus during packaging, and they are not easy to remove.

Consumers also do not like this mucus, and although the mushroom has an excellent taste, not everyone decides to buy it precisely because of this feature.

We packed Nameko in 7-ounce trays so that particles of the substrate remained on the tips of the legs – something like selling tomato seedlings. In this case, the mushrooms could be stored for two weeks without problems.

If the lower part of the leg was cut off, it rotted literally after 2-3 days.

In Japan and China, Nameko is grown in jars; therefore, the mushrooms are cut off at the very neck when harvesting.

But the point is that their further fate is freezing or blanching.

If you study market information for Asian countries, you can see what huge volumes of this mushroom are sold and exported.

While in Europe, we visually analyzed the preserved mushrooms sold in so-called Russian stores. Nameko was most often sold under the guise of pickled honey mushrooms. In some positions, it was still indicated that these are "Honey mushrooms Nameko," although they do not belong to such a group.

The same conservation was often found on Russian trading floors.

In general, I don't see anything objectionable here.

Not every buyer who sees such a jar will understand what "Nameko Pickled Pholiota" is. But Honey Nameko is more understandable; they are similar and are not inferior in shape and taste.

Realizing this trend, we came up with a great business idea: to grow Nameko in large enough volumes for further processing in pickled form.

We agreed with our colleague from Zaporizhzhia, who was producing substrate for sale, that my wife and I would develop the substrate technology for Nameko`s production of substrate blocks. Then we proposed this idea to colleagues at one company that grew champignons.

By that time, they had free cells. So, we planned to grow Nameko for conservation, with a volume of 3 tons per month, with a subsequent increase in productivity.

This company has already begun installing its mushroom processing workshop, and this idea has taken on even more exciting forms.

Like many other things, the war prevented this idea from becoming a reality. A new tragic reality has arrived.

So, we put this business idea aside until better times.

Nameko Cultivation.

Substrate:

Option #1

1.Sawdust from deciduous trees – 80%

2.Wheat bran – 20%

3.Chalk, gypsum 0.5+0.5, only 1%

4.Substrate humidity 62-65%

Option #2

1.Sawdust from deciduous trees – 60%

2.Wheat straw or sunflower husk pellets – 20%

3.Soybean husk – 20%

4.Chalk, gypsum 0.5+0.5, only 1%

5.Substrate humidity 62-65%

The incubation period under our conditions was about 25-29 days at a temperature in the incubator chamber of +22-23°C (72-75°F) Do not allow the substrate in the center of the block to heat above +25°C (78°F).

A fully ripe block mushroom is beige, with yellow exudate on the surface.

When transferring blocks from the incubator to the growth chamber, try not to damage the surface layer of the substrate.

If Nameko is cultivated separately in monoculture, you can immediately open the block, leaving a collar 3-4 inches high. Then, the humidity in the chamber must be set to 100%, temperature +10-13°C (50-57°F), and illumination 500 lux.

If you plan to grow with other mushrooms, then it is better to keep it for one or two weeks, without opening the package, at a temperature of +10-15°C (50-59°F), and after orange mucus appears on the surface, open it. Mucus is a harbinger of the formation of primordia on it. It should always be kept moist. If it is impossible to maintain the humidity in the chamber close to 100%, then light irrigation of the substrate is necessary without the formation of stagnant water on it.

Another option is to wait for the formation of primordia under the film without opening the package and only then open it when the primordia is about 50% of the surface.

Primordia appears on the surface after approximately two weeks. Harvesting begins in another 7-10 days.

The yield very often reaches 30-35%. Collecting the mushroom on time is necessary to keep it from opening. Usually, by postponing picking for an hour or two, you can end up with mushrooms that have already been opened and will not have the best presentation.

The first wave ready for harvest, M4190

On spent Nameko blocks, outdoors, in natural conditions, magnificent forest mushrooms will grow. It is what we like to eat precisely. They are not different from those who grew up in the forest.

Mushrooms collected outside

CHAPTER 42

Medicinal Mushrooms

We paid particular attention to the so-called medicinal mushrooms. The entire line of mushrooms we grow has beneficial, preventive, and medicinal properties. These properties generally strengthen the immune system of our body. But there is a separate line of mushrooms that can be used more specifically for preventive and therapeutic purposes. These crops have been known for a long time, especially in China, Japan, and Korea, which are the leading countries in this direction.

For this purpose, we grew Hericium, Reishi, and the common Shiitake, with its polysaccharide Lentinan.

A comment:

Lentinan polysaccharide is a biologically active substance extracted from the Lentinula edodes mushroom, also known as Shiitake. Shiitake is widely used in Asian cuisine and is known for its medicinal properties. Lentinan is one of these mushroom's main components, attracting attention due to its potential immunomodulatory and antitumor properties.

Research shows that lentinan may stimulate the immune system, helping fight infections and suppress tumor growth. This polysaccharide also has anti-inflammatory properties and may help treat various inflammation-related diseases.

Lentinan is being investigated as a potential anti-cancer agent, although its effectiveness and safety require further clinical studies. However, its use as a dietary supplement or a component of certain medications may be beneficial in supporting a healthy immune system and well-being.

In the Lion's mane mushroom (Hericium) it is a beta-glucan

The polysaccharide commonly found in the Hericium mushroom is called beta-glucan. It is a family of polysaccharides found in various mushrooms, including Hericium. Beta-glucans are known for their potential anti-inflammatory, immunomodulatory, and antioxidant properties.

Research shows that beta-glucans may support a healthy immune system by stimulating its function and helping the body fight infection and disease. They may also have positive effects on the digestive system and metabolism.

Hericium mushrooms, such as Hericium erinaceus, are often used in Chinese medicine and other cultures as dietary supplements or herbs to support health. Due to the presence of beta-glucans, they may have several potential health-promoting properties.

Flammulina, rich in the polysaccharide flammulin, is equal to these mushrooms in terms of usefulness.

Flammulin, also known as flammulin beta-glucan, is one of the significant polysaccharides found in the mushroom Flammulina velutipes, also known as honey mushroom. This mushroom is widely used in Asian cuisine and is known for its potential medicinal properties.

Flammulin beta-glucan has various biological activities, including immunomodulatory, anti-inflammatory, and antioxidant properties. Research shows it may help strengthen the immune system, stimulate its function, and help the body fight infection and disease.

In addition, flammulin has potential antitumor properties and may help prevent or treat cancer. Some studies suggest it may benefit cardiovascular health and help lower blood cholesterol levels.

Numerous studies and clinical trials are still needed to confirm its effectiveness and safety, and flammulin beta-glucan is of interest as a potential dietary supplement and drug.

There is a story or parable:

The story is associated with the Japanese village of Nagano and its residents, who often consumed honey mushrooms (Flammulina velutipes) containing polysaccharides, including the beta-glucan flammulin. This village was known for its low cancer rates, attracting researchers` attention.

Although the story is not scientifically proven, many studies in subsequent years have shown the potential anti-cancer properties of the beta-glucan flammulin.

Some studies have shown that regular consumption of mushrooms, such as honey, may be linked with a reduced risk of cancer and other diseases due to their immunomodulatory and antioxidant properties.

While this story may be an exciting example of the potential benefits of consuming honey mushrooms and its components, such as the beta-glucan flammulin, it should be viewed more as a cultural aspect than as evidence of scientific fact. Additional clinical studies are required to confirm the direct link between Honey mushroom consumption and reduced cancer risk.

Well, simply unique – Reishi mushroom

Reishi (or Ganoderma lucidum) is a mushroom widely used in traditional medicine, especially in Asian countries such as China and Japan. It contains several biologically active substances, including polysaccharides and beta-glucans.

The beta-glucans found in Reishi are known for their immunomodulatory properties. They can stimulate the activity of various immune system cells, such as macrophages, neutrophils, and natural killers, which help strengthen immune function and fight infections.

In addition, Reishi contains other biologically active substances, such as terpenes, polysaccharides, amino acids, and peptides, which may also have positive health effects.

Potential health benefits associated with consuming Reishi include:

1. **Strengthening the immune system:** Beta-glucans and other bioactive substances may help enhance the body's natural defense mechanisms.

2. **Anti-inflammatory properties:** Reishi can reduce inflammation due to its antioxidant and anti-inflammatory properties.

3. **Heart health support:** Some studies indicate that Reishi may help lower cholesterol and blood pressure, promoting heart health.

4. **Anti-cancer activity:** Some studies suggest that Reishi may have potential as an anti-cancer agent, although more research is required to confirm these results.

Please consult a qualified physician or nutritionist before changing your diet or taking supplements.

We have studied the crops well, successfully grown them, and used tinctures, powders, and water decoctions. Hericium, Shiitake, and Flamulina are excellent in cooking.

Moreover, I note again that Flammulina is one of our favorite mushrooms. Although... well, how can you say which of your children is the most beloved? They are all beautiful in their own way. I don't know if I made a successful allegory.

We sold these mushrooms in fresh, dried form and powders.

We had a separate category of buyers, consumers of such products, who were interested in the health benefits of these mushrooms. The prices for the entire line of these products were very high.

CHAPTER 43

Lion's Mane (Hericium Erinaceus)

It has an incredibly original mushroom shape, taste, medicinal and preventive properties.

The fruiting bodies of Hericium are rich in phosphorus and potassium. They also contain vitamins B1, B2, B12, nicotinic acid, and provitamin D2, which promote calcium metabolism and prevent the formation of osteoporosis.

Several bioactive substances have been identified, such as hericenones and erinacins, which have an antitumor effect, can restore degenerative neuronal disorders, and regenerate peripheral nerve fibers.

Hericium is an edible mushroom and has excellent medicinal value. It has been used successfully in Chinese medicine and cooking for hundreds of years.

Hericium is used successfully to treat liver dysfunction, Alzheimer's and Parkinson's diseases, and wound healing. Eating mushrooms improves memory and sleep quality and reveals cognitive abilities. Clinical studies have proven successful in treating the effects of schizophrenia and alleviating the symptoms of menopause; the properties of this mushroom help prevent thrombosis, heart attacks, and strokes.

Hericium is used in cooking, raw form, water infusion, dried mushroom powder, and alcohol tincture. This mushroom also regulates blood glucose, triglycerides, and cholesterol levels.

Growing technology

Hericium is grown on sawdust of deciduous trees and waste from agricultural grain crops.

Optimal substrate performance: humidity 58-61%; pH 5.0-6.5; total nitrogen content 0.8-1.0%; C/N ratio 70-90/1; density 0,5-0,6kg/m3 (0.031-0.037lb/ft^3).

The grain mycelium application rate is 1.5-3% of the mycelium mass.

In our case, we used the same substrate as for Shiitake.

Incubation: 25-30 days. The overgrowth rate depends on the block's mass and strain: temperature +21-23°C (70-75°F); humidity 85-90%; CO_2 0.5-3.0%.

Formation of primordia: 5-8d; temperature +13-15°C (57-60°F); humidity 95-98%; CO_2 0.5-0.7%; lighting 500-1000lux.

Cuts are made on the bag, and the free edge of the bag is fixed to avoid germination under the tape to form primordia.

Fruiting: 7-10th day; temperature +16-22°C (60-72°F); humidity 90-95%; CO_2 500-1000 ppm.

Collect mushrooms carefully, twisting or cutting so as not to damage the delicate ridges of the fruiting body. They are pretty elastic, but traces of mechanical impact may remain. Mushrooms can be stored packaged in the refrigerator at +0.5-3°C (33-37°F) for up to 14 days or immediately prepared for drying.

The productivity of Hericium is up to 300g (10.5 ounces) of fresh mushrooms from 1kg (2.2 pounds) of substrate.

We tried many different strains. Some tasted bitter, others were not snow-white, and others did not have large fruits. After much experimentation, we isolated an excellent strain, 977, from the Kholodny Institute of Botany in Ukraine. We grow it to this day.

On our farm, Hericium grew well in the same chamber with King oyster mushrooms and Shiitake.

When you harvest Hericium, there is a strong aroma of wild mushrooms around you. Indeed, Hericium does not look like an ordinary mushroom. It has a strong mushroom aroma.

If desired, and for health prevention, it can be consumed raw.

When cooked, it develops an aroma and taste similar to seafood. The consistency is delicate, like marmalade. It is better to cook with butter.

Part of the Hericium harvest was sold fresh, and its price was very high.

We also dried it and used tinctures and decoctions. It was sold to order at a high price.

These are the packages we delivered exclusive orders in

Hericium was easy to dry and could be stored in sealed bags for a long

Tincture for health

CHAPTER 44

Reishi Mushroom (Polypore Lacquered, Ganoderma Lacquered), Lat. Ganoderma Lucidum

Reishi (Polypore lacquered, Ganoderma lacquered), lat. Ganoderma lucidum is a mushroom of the Ganoderma genus of the Ganoderma-taceae family. In China and Korea, the mushroom is known as "Ling-zhi" (Mushroom/herb of immortality). In Japan, this mushroom is best known as "Reishi" (mushroom of spiritual power) and "Mannentake" (ten-thousand-year-old mushroom).

The cap's color varies from reddish to brownish-violet or (sometimes) black, with a yellowish tint and visible growth rings. The pulp is very dense and woody.

USEFUL PROPERTIES: The fruiting bodies and mycelium of Ganoderma lucidum contain carbohydrates (reducing sugars and polysaccharides), amino acids, peptides, proteins, and triterpenes, including steroids, lipids, alkaloids, glycosides, volatile essential oils, vitamins, and trace elements such as magnesium, manganese, molybdenum, calcium, zinc, potassium, sodium, iron, copper, sulfur, and germanium.

Germanium, found in high concentrations in the fruiting bodies of Ganoderma lucidum, is found in the organic compound carboxyethyl germanium sesquioxide. Polysaccharides and triterpenes are the most important biologically active compounds isolated from this mushroom. Almost all the preventive and therapeutic effects known from the lacquered tinder fungus were found in these two groups of compounds. Intensive studies of Ganoderma lucidum over the past decades have shown that biologically active substances isolated from this fungus have immunomodulatory, antitumor, antiviral, antibiotic, hypolipidemic, hypoglycemic, hepatoprotective, genoprotective, anti-inflammatory, anti-allergenic, antioxidant effects, and can regulate the functioning of the cardiovascular system, respiratory and nervous systems.

Medicines based on lingzhi dilate the heart`s coronary artery, enrich the blood with oxygen, eliminate coronary heart disease, prevent myocardial infarction, and normalize cardiac activity. It is used for various diseases, including bronchial asthma, neurasthenia, gastritis, and liver diseases.

The introduction of Reishi mushroom into the diet also helps to raise mental and physical performance and increase the human body's resistance to the harmful effects of various unfavorable environmental factors (such as cold, heat, ionizing radiation, climate or atmospheric pressure changes, adverse environmental conditions, low levels of oxygen). This effect of the Reishi mushroom is because it belongs to the class of "adaptogen" plants. In its ability to mobilize the internal energy reserves of the human body and increase the body's endurance under conditions of intense stress, mental, physical, and psycho-emotional stress, Reishi mushroom is not inferior to such powerful natural adaptogens as ginseng, mumiyo, Rhodiola rosea, Schisandra chinensis.

The easiest way to use Reishi is to pour 2 teaspoons of chopped mushroom into 200ml (1 glass) of water, bring it to a boil, and simmer for 5 minutes with constant stirring. Then, let the broth sit for 30 minutes, strain, cool, and take it three times a day 30 minutes before meals.

Reishi is not edible.

They are grown exclusively as a medicinal mushroom.

We grew it only in the warm season and in separate rooms, which were sometimes unsuitable for growing. The main thing to understand is that it loves a hot tropical climate. Therefore, raising it in winter or off-season is impossible when we grow edible mushrooms. It is necessary to create a tropical environment for it: temperature +20-26°C (68-80°F), and humidity 95-99%. There should be practically no air movement in the chamber. That is, the chamber should be humid, hot, and stuffy.

The substrate is the same as for shiitake.

Its incubation period is 50-60 days.

The substrate is ready for fruiting when a brown-black crust has formed on top.

It is just the time to initiate fruiting.

We place it in a chamber with a temperature of +22-26°C (72-80°F) and a humidity of 90-98%.

Primordia appears on the 20th to 30th day. After another 20-30 days, the mushrooms can be collected. The mushroom is in development, and there is a white border on the edges of its cap. As soon as this edging disappears, the mushroom is considered mature and stops growing.

The substrate surface is often loved by flies, laying larvae in it. But Nadya found an effortless and effective way against these pests. You need to dilute a light pink solution of potassium permanganate and pour it over the entire surface of the substrate. For this purpose, when cutting the film, we always left a small collar of film. It made it possible to pour a certain amount of such a solution to cover the entire surface. The larvae in this solution are paralyzed, and no further development occurs.

This system worked flawlessly, allowing the blocks to bear fruit for a long time. Otherwise, the larvae destroyed the mycelium, and the block was rotting and had to be disposed of.

To avoid these problems, we have also developed an option for fruiting on the side of the block. With this technology, one cap grew without a stem, as in nature, on a tree trunk. But this version's top of the block was closed and not exposed to midges.

When fruiting, the mushroom releases a lot of spores, similar to cocoa powder. Therefore, if any other mushrooms grow nearby, they will be covered with these brown spores.

A layer of spores, sometimes even 1mm (0.03 inch) thick, lies everywhere – on shelves, blocks, floors, and mushrooms.

That is a beautiful mushroom, like one from a fairy tale. No two fruiting bodies are alike. You can observe this mushroom for a long time; its forms are unusual and fascinating. The lacquered structure adds mystery to this mushroom.

It is sold exclusively to order for those who are interested in consuming mushrooms for treatment and prevention.

We also used tinctures and decoctions from it.

I even added Reishi powder to my coffee.

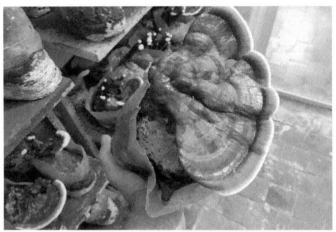

Lateral fruiting

Shape of mushrooms during lateral fruiting

Sending packaged Reishi to customers

CHAPTER 45

Stropharia

This mushroom came into our collection by accident. Colleagues from the Melitopol laboratory of mycelium production gave us one package of working Stropharia mycelium. They then grew a small batch for someone to order.

We propagated it for ourselves. We had been interested in this mushroom for a long time, but it was not on the commercial line, so somehow, we never got around to it. And then there was such luck, so it was only possible to take advantage of the opportunity.

We knew the peculiarities of cultivating Stropharia in general, but in theory, all that remained was to try everything with our hands.

We conducted a series of experiments to grow Stropharia in different ways.

In this book, we will provide a short photo report.

You can read a more detailed description of our technology in the next book dedicated to this mushroom culture.

The first mushrooms

Whole mushroom family

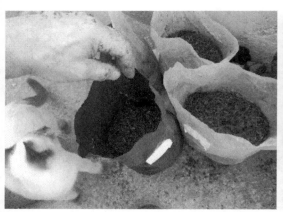

Stropharia was good friends with Shiitake, but they were on the same shelf

CHAPTER 46

Mushroom Platter

We have developed a new direction for the sale of mushrooms. We are discussing packaging different mushroom cultures, also called assorted substrates.

We formed an assortment of different types of mushrooms and packaged them in one tray. These sets looked simply delicious and flavorful. The process itself also brought creative pleasure. I won't say that we had large quantities of assorted supplies, but they were always in demand from their customers. Even if one batch with one type of mushroom included several assorted packages, such a batch always attracted attention. They could also sell well at the market, where the buyer wanted to try different mushrooms.

Such assortments are well-bought by restaurants and are just as quickly consumed by people when they want to try different flavors of mushrooms.

Large companies do not do this because the product is individually made. But for a family farm, this is an exciting option.

Moreover, the assortment can be combined from different types of mushrooms, and the buyer will pick the desired one.

When you add Shiitake, Oyster mushrooms, King oyster mushrooms, Nameko, a sprig of rosemary, or a bay leaf to the colorful variety, it will be impossible to pass by such beauty.

Compiling and packaging such compositions was a pleasure for my wife and me.

In the photo, we presented only some variations of such packaging.

CHAPTER 47

Sale of Substrate Blocks (Kits for Growing Mushrooms)

This topic is gaining momentum. More and more people want to grow mushrooms from the kit in their kitchen, bathroom, windowsill, or garden plot.

There is room for the manufacturer's imagination and ideas. We didn't stand aside, either. We already had extensive experience in this direction when we worked at mushroom-growing enterprises in Kyiv. We sold blocks of all types of mushrooms grown on our farm.

We created color instructions for growing each crop. For those who bought several blocks simultaneously, another substrate block was often added as a gift. We made gift sets that included a tray with moss and a block of Shiitake, decorating this set thematically.

Then we got dealers, which made our job more manageable. Every day, I delivered dozens of blocks to the post office. Sales overgrew, and this direction significantly increased total income.

We have already begun to think about expanding this area. Selling a finished block is one thing, but growing mushrooms from it and selling them is another.

The price of such blocks was tens of times higher than their cost and several times higher than the wholesale price of the substrate. It was an individual order, exclusive. People did not plan to receive income from purchasing such a block. They just liked to grow mushrooms on their own, like flowers.

With certain advertising, this area is developing and popularizing very quickly.

Shiitake growing kit

King oyster mushrooms grown on blocks in the garden under the trees

From time to time, we received significant orders for entire batches of blocks.

My wife Nadya communicated with our dealers in this direction and formed an order. I selected the blocks, put them in the car, and took them to the courier service department. Workers quickly packed everything, and the order was sent to the recipient.

It brought in significant income.

A batch of substrate blocks leaves for the customer

CHAPTER 48

Manufacturing Filter Bags

To form substrate blocks, bags with a HEPA breathing filter are used. The filter has a throughput of 0.2-0.5 microns and allows particles no less than this value to pass through. Such parameters allow the substrate to breathe through the filter, and infection in the form of mold spores and bacteria cannot get inside.

Many such packages are sold in the USA, Europe, and China. But they all cost 0.35 to 1.0 dollars, depending on the quantity.

It is a reasonably high price, constituting a significant share of the cost of the entire unit.

At the beginning of the book, I wrote that we have developed our technology for producing bags whose price will be around 0.05 or even less dollars.

Our colleague from Ukraine designed a machine that solders a filter element into a polyethylene bag.

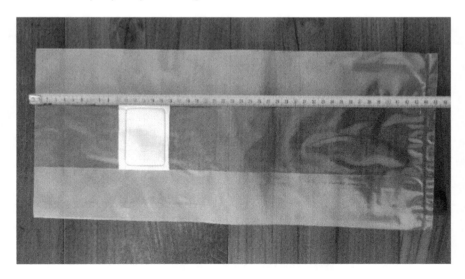

But it is more suitable for medium-sized enterprises. Our unique method was perfect for our small farm.

As I wrote earlier, since we use atmospheric sterilization at a temperature of +100°C (212°F), we can use cheaper polyethylene bags versus polypropylene bags for a temperature of +120-125°C (248-257°F).

Recently, we concluded supplies of plastic bags made from recycled materials are even cheaper than bags made from primary raw materials.

The process of bag gluing technology is as follows:

- Purchase double-sided tape, 40-50 ml (1-2 inches) wide.

- Squares are cut from it, measuring 50x50 (2x2) or 40x40 (1x1). These squares are glued with one adhesive side to the bag.

- Then, a punch makes an 18-20ml (0.7-0.8-inch) hole, which pierces both the bag and the tape.

- Then, pieces of the filter membrane are cut, the same size as the squares of adhesive tape.

- The protective film of the second adhesive layer of tape is removed, and the filter is glued.

- The adhesive tape must be of good quality.

- Various building breathable membranes are suitable as membranes. There are a large number of them on the market.

We liked the materials from Tyvek the most.

That's it, the package is ready. Instead of a punch, you can use a stapler. The photo shows how this happens. You can cut squares of tape with scissors or purchase a unique dispenser.

We had assigned responsibilities. Nadya would stick the tape, I would punch a hole, and Nadya or I would then stick the filter on.

We did all this in the evening or at lunch, in front of the TV while relaxing.

But we saved significantly on the price.

The photo review clearly shows the sequence of actions according to my description.

Punching a hole

Removing the protective film of the second adhesive layer

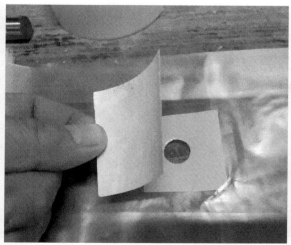

Gluing a piece of 5x5cm Tyvek membrane

Filter bags are ready for further use

CHAPTER 49

Product Storage

It is a crucial component of the production process.

Depending on how correctly you organize this process and adhere to the regulations, you can keep mushrooms suitable for sale for as long as possible, making it more convenient to plan sales.

The first and central condition is to place the mushrooms in the refrigerator immediately after picking them at a temperature of +1-2°C (33-35°F) for rapid cooling. It is advisable to use small boxes with good ventilation at this time.

If you keep up to 3kg (6.6 pounds) of mushrooms in boxes, they will cool on average in 30-50 minutes to the temperature, after which they can be packaged.

Next, after cooling, it is **necessary** to package the mushrooms in trays using packaging film. If this is not done, then daily weight loss can be up to 5%. That's quite a lot, and it's your money.

The room where the mushrooms are packaged should be pretty cool, no higher than +16°C (60°F). Mushrooms must be taken out of the refrigerator in boxes in small batches so that during the packaging process, they are in the room for no more than 10-15 minutes and then quickly put into the refrigerator.

This regulation will allow you to store good-quality mushrooms for up to two weeks maximum. Of course, the most acceptable sales period is 7-10 days, considering that the mushrooms will be sold in the store for some time.

CHAPTER 50

Refrigerator

I made the refrigeration chamber using slats and polystyrene foam boards on the same principle as the growing rooms. It looked like an extension to the substrate area, with the same concept, so that all production premises were as close to each other as possible.

A second-hand split system air conditioner was first used as a refrigeration unit. But then I returned to the time-tested window air conditioners of the BK-2500 series. They always amazed me with their absolute reliability.

I dismantled their standard automation and installed the same time-tested, simple, reliable temperature controllers.

Thus, I bought a very inexpensive refrigerator for less than $700, which can store up to 1102 pounds of mushrooms and mycelium.

Refrigerator control system using simple controllers

The refrigerator compartment could accommodate up to 550 kg of mushrooms, and the temperature could be maintained at +2-6°C

The dimensions of the refrigerator and its power must be calculated based on the conditions under which mycelium reserves must be preserved.

CHAPTER 51

Farm Structure and Production Business Model

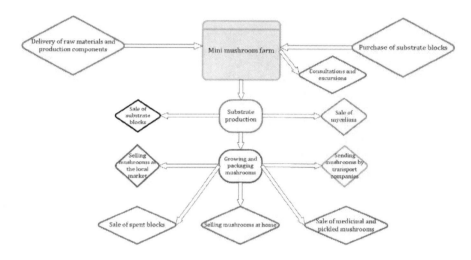

Now we'll tell you how our business was organized.

Business plan

At the beginning of the book, we mentioned that our farm`s main goal was to create a profitable enterprise capable of producing 500 kg (1102 pounds) of packaged mushrooms monthly. To do this, we made 2500-3000kg (5511-6613) pounds of high-quality substrate.

In addition, as the volume of orders increased, we purchased substrate from fellow manufacturers. This allowed us to improve the substrate volume by another 2000kg (4409 pounds) and, accordingly, additionally produce 300-400kg (661-881 pounds) of mushrooms monthly.

Thanks to low energy consumption in all production cycles, the absence of hired workers, well-planned logistics, efficient work with customers, and delivery service, we achieved high profitability quickly.

In addition to the sale of fresh packaged mushrooms, additional income was generated by:

1.sale of substrate blocks

2.sale of mycelium

3.sale of medicinal and pickled mushrooms

4.sale of used substrate blocks

5.consultations and excursions

We accepted orders for the current week based on requests from local vegetable stores and our dealers in Kyiv and Zaporizhzhia. The product was delivered to local stores two to three times a week and sent to dealers by postal companies once or twice a week.

Our range of medicinal mushrooms included dried and fresh Hericium, Ganoderma, and Shiitake, which were also in demand. The prices for these products were relatively high.

To trade substrate blocks for home cultivation, we accepted pre-orders and sent them by transport companies. This area was actively developing as more and more people showed interest in growing mushrooms at home using mushroom kits.

Spent blocks were also in demand among summer residents. They could be taken to mulch the soil and make compost. Some also grew mushrooms on these blocks in shade gardens. We shipped such blocks twice a week by calling in advance.

If you cannot organize the sale of used blocks, you must take care of their disposal in advance. You will have to deal with large volumes of waste blocks that need to be disposed of somewhere or disposed of. What are the options?

If you have enough space on your site, you can organize compost heaps for your garden's needs. However, spent blocks are still living organisms, and bacteria do not efficiently process them. Therefore, composting should be carried out using active methods. For example, treat blocks with EM solutions containing beneficial bacteria, which speed up the processing process.

It is also worth considering that compost heaps should be built no higher than one meter to ensure sufficient aeration for the activity of beneficial aerobic bacteria.

Unique mechanisms for breaking blocks can also help with recycling.

Unit for crushing and separating waste blocks

Such aggregates break up the substrate block and separate it from the film. There is a sufficient variety of such mechanisms on trading platforms in China.

At one enterprise we worked, an agreement was concluded with a company that processed organic raw materials. The company also picked up used blocks for free using its transport.

In general, when planning a business, the issue of recycling waste substrate blocks must be considered.

Sometimes, we organized excursions to our farm.

These excursions were paid for and popularized our business. We showed visitors our growing chambers and the whole process. Of course, at the end of the excursion, there was a mushroom dinner and gifts. Such excursions always went well for all participants.

We also provided paid consultations on growing technology online and on-site at our farm.

As experienced mushroom growers, we could ensure the planting of various crops on our farm. If you need more experience, then in the first year, you should limit yourself to two or three crops in demand on the market and conduct experiments with the rest to get to know them in the future. Of course, a large assortment of products at the enterprise automatically increases sales volumes. It is a proven truth. However, the assortment must be approached gradually, gaining experience. It is necessary for growing mushrooms to become a business for you. But you learn this quickly because those ready for business are motivated and purposeful.

Manufacturing process

The substrate production cycle was daily. This schedule also included mycelium production work. The loading schedule for growing chambers with substrate blocks was drawn up for a year, a quarter, and a month. This schedule has been adjusted to reflect holiday trading. In this case, we consider the increase in sales during the holidays, especially during the Christmas holidays. These days, sales double or more times, so plans for sowing substrate blocks and placing them in growing chambers must be considered in advance.

The whole working day included:

1. Morning mushroom picking.

2. Preparation and soaking of the substrate composition.

3. Inoculation of sterilized blocks.

4. Transfer of inoculated blocks to the incubator.

5. Unloading sterilized blocks into the clean room.

6. Mushroom packaging.

7. Delivery of orders.

8. Manufacturing of substrate blocks and loading of sterilizers.

9. Making bags with filters.

10. Evening picking and packing of mushrooms.

CHAPTER 52

The Final Is an Occupation

We were actively developing and building business plans and believing in our strengths and capabilities. But the morning of February 24, 2022, brought a change we could not have foreseen.

My wife Nadya was still sleeping, and I was already in the cell, collecting Shiitakes. Suddenly, the ground shook underfoot, and the air filled with fear. These were explosions that thundered not far from our town. Turning on the TV, we realized that life as we knew it was now divided into BEFORE and AFTER. A new stage in life has begun. That is war...

Our town was occupied a few days later.

It became scary to stay, and we decided to leave while we still had the opportunity. We left our house, belongings, mushroom blocks in the incubator, and chambers full of growing mushrooms. All this has already lost its value.

That is how we left our house and mushroom farm

Having loaded the essentials and taken our two cats into the car, we embarked on a dangerous and long journey to the unoccupied part of Ukraine. We needed to get to Zaporizhzhya.

The road was terrible and tense, among destroyed villages, through military checkpoints of the occupiers. There were often broken tanks and cars standing along the sides of the road, and military equipment of the occupiers drove past us. Just before Zaporizhzhia, we came under mortar fire.

Although the mines exploded at a sufficient distance from us, this caused the car to be thrown from side to side, and fragments and pieces of earth flew toward us.

And here we are in Zaporizhzhia. We were met by Ukrainian soldiers and escorted to a temporary camp, where we were fed and given food to our animals. Next, our path lay to the Vinnytsia region.

We could not believe that after so much effort and energy invested in our home and production, we would have to give it all up and leave everything at the peak of our achievements.

We had to leave everything, and our future fate was unknown.

In our hearts, we hoped that all this was temporary and that we would return soon. That was just a terrible dream that we would soon wake up from.

However, later, we learned that the occupying soldiers had settled in our house. They broke down the doors, looted the house, and took away everything valuable. The understanding that this would most likely last for a long time, and perhaps forever, became increasingly pronounced, and we hoped less and less to return.

We lived as refugees in the Vinnytsia region for some time. During this time, we advised mushroom growers from Israel, Moldova, and Montenegro. After some time, we were invited to Montenegro to work as technologists at a large enterprise under construction for growing Shiitake mushrooms.

CHAPTER 53

The Way to Montenegro

We realized that life does not stand still and we need to continue to move forward, so we agreed and began to prepare for the trip. Sunny Montenegro and interesting work awaited us. It took two days to travel.

We drove to the border along the Zhytomyr highway, already popularly called the "Road of Death." On this route, Russian tanks shot down many civilian vehicles, with people fleeing the war. Along the entire route, we saw destroyed and burned houses, gas stations, and bridges.

We are ready to travel to Montenegro

On the border of Montenegro

And now we are in a new place, at a new enterprise, in Montenegro, with new plans, new forces, and pain in our souls for our home and Ukraine.

Montenegro has opened its hospitable arms to us. But this is the beginning of our new story in the mushroom business, which we will discuss in the next book.

At the new production

Modern equipment on a mushroom farm

Dear reader,

Thank you for your attention to our story. I look forward to seeing you in the next book!

In the next book, you will find exciting materials, in which we describe the experience of a large modern production facility, where we fully realize our potential as technologists and specialists in growing exotic mushrooms.

Dear readers, see you in the next book.

Sincerely, Serge Honcharov and Nadiya Honcharova.
Ukraine.

CHAPTER 54

Recipe

I love to cook, and especially dishes with mushrooms.

I cannot say I'm a pro or cook according to recipes. But I like to experiment and get different tastes. Moreover, mushrooms are always available, and a desire is often to try something new. Our diet usually has regular fried mushrooms with various sauces and seasonings.

We are preparing a separate book with our recipes.

Here, we present one of the recipes without which we cannot do any outdoor recreation.

King oyster mushroom on barbecue

There are several comments for this dish.

Pre-soak mushrooms in soy sauce for 30-40 minutes.

Place on the grill so that pieces of lard are placed on top.

No salt is needed, as soy sauce is salty enough.

We would be happy if you, dear readers, would leave a review of the book on Amazon.

LITERATURE

1. **TECHNOLOGICAL PRINCIPLES FOR THE INTRODUCTION OF WINTER MUSHROOM (FLAMMULINA VELUTIPES (CURTIS) SINGER) INTO THE INDUSTRIAL CULTURE**
No. 5 (87), 2020 Scientific reports of NULES of Ukraine ISSN 2223-1609 UDC 635.82
I. I. Bandura, Candidate of Agricultural Sciences, Associate Professor
orcid.org/0000-0001-7835-3293
Tavria State Agrotechnological University
named after Dmytro Motornyi
H. A. BISKO, Doctor of Biological Sciences, Professor
orcid.org/0000-0003-1894-0896
M.G. Kholodny Institute of Botany of the National Academy of Sciences of Ukraine
A. S. KULYK, Candidate of Technical Sciences, Associate Professor
orcid.org/0000-0001-5403-3084
Tavria State Agrotechnological University
named after Dmytro Motornyi
O. M. Tsyz, Candidate of Agricultural Sciences, Associate Professor
orcid.org/0000-0001-7174-7011
National University of Life and Environmental Sciences of Ukraine
C. V. Chausov, Candidate of Technical Sciences, Associate Professor
orcid.org/0000-0003-3811-9077
Tavria State Agrotechnological University
Dmytro Motornyi Tavria State Agrotechnological University
O. VASILENKO, Zhovtneve Farm, Kyiv, Ukraine
orcid.org/0000-0002-2449-6456
S.GONCHAROV, individual entrepreneur **S. Goncharov**
orcid.org/0000-0001-6733-701X
doi.org/10.31548/dopovidi2020.05.004

2. **LESS COMMON VEGETABLE PLANTS AND MUSHROOMS: A TUTORIAL MANUAL.**
- 2nd ed. supplemented and revised / O.V. Khareba, O.I. Ulyanych,
V.V. Khareba, Z.I. Kovtunyuk, I.I. Bandura, N.V. Vorobyova,
O.M. Tsyz, V.V. Yatsenko. Vinnytsia: Nilan Ltd, 2021. 256 c.
ISBN 978-966-924-881-7

3. **INFLUENCE OF THE SUBSTRATE COMPOSITION ON THE YIELD AND NUTRITIONAL VALUE OF THE FRUITING BODIES OF THE EDIBLE MUSHROOMS PLEUROTUS CITRINOPILEATUS AND CYCLOCYBE AEGERITA**
UDK 001:[631.5+635.8+ 579.6+582.28+ 664.8/.9
06.01.06 - vegetable growing 20 Agricultural sciences and food ABSTRACT of the dissertation for the degree of Doctor of Science Uman – 2023

Iryna Bandura

Made in United States
Troutdale, OR
11/13/2024

24736713R00142